CINEMA PARADISO

Cinema Paradiso

GIUSEPPE TORNATORE

faber and faber
LONDON · BOSTON

First published in 1994 by Faber and Faber Limited
3 Queen Square London WCIN 3AU

This edition as part of a boxed-set with the video *Cinema Paradiso*. Not for resale

Photoset by Parker Typesetting Service Ltd, Leicester
Printed in England by Clays Ltd, St Ives plc

Cover photo courtesey of BFI Stills, Posters and Design

A CIP record of this book is available from the British Library

ISBN 0-571-17674-7

2 4 6 8 10 9 7 5 3 1

The cast of *Cinema Paradiso* includes:

ALFREDO	Philippe Noiret
SALVATORE (adult)	Jacques Perrin
SALVATORE (child)	Salvatore Cascio
SALVATORE (adolescent)	Marco Leonardi
ELENA (adolescent)	Agnese Nano
ELENA (adult)	Brigitte Fossey
MARIA (young)	Antonella Attili
MARIA (old)	Pupella Maggio
FATHER ADELFIO	Leopoldo Trieste

Director of Photography	Blasco Giurato
Production Designer	Andrea Crisanti
Costume Designer	Beatrice Bordone
Editor	Mario Morra
Music	Ennio Morricone
Love Theme	Andrea Morricone
Screenplay	Guiseppe Tornatore
Producer	Franco Cristaldi
Director	Guiseppe Tornatore

1: GIANCALDO. SALVATORE'S MOTHER'S HOUSE. EXT/
INT. DAY
*The October sun slashes through the grey clouds, cuts across the
shadow towards the sea, along the coast where the new suburbs of the
city of Giancaldo have been built up.*
*Bright light streams through the windows, glancing off the white
walls in an almost blinding reflection.* MARIA, *a woman a little over
sixty, is trying to find somebody on the phone.*
MARIA: . . . Salvatore, that's right, Salvatore. Di Vita Salvatore
. . . But, miss, what do you mean you don't know him?! . . .
I . . . Yes . . .
(*She gives a nervous sigh. She has dialled her way through
endless numbers but still hasn't managed to speak to Mr Di
Vita. She finally heaves a sigh of relief.*)
. . . That's right, good for you! Oh! . . . yes . . . And I'm his
mother. I'm calling from Sicily. Been trying all day . . . Ah,
he's not there . . . But would you be so kind as to give me
. . .? . . . Yes . . .
(*She nods at another woman around forty sitting nearby: it is
LIA, her daughter, who jots down the numbers her mother
dictates:*)
. . . Six, five, six, two, two, oh, six . . . Thanks ever so
much . . . Goodbye. Goodbye.
(*She hangs up, takes the number* LIA *has jotted down,
determined to have still another try.* LIA *speaks to her as if she
were a baby, to be more convincing.*)
LIA: Look, Ma . . . It's useless calling him. He'll be terribly
busy, God knows where he is. Besides he might not even
remember. Do as I say, forget it . . . He hasn't been here
for thirty years. You know how he is.
(MARIA *pauses to think it over. The decision she has to make is
important. Then, stubbornly:*)
MARIA: He'll remember! He'll remember!
(*She puts on her glasses and starts dialling the number.*)
. . . I'm positive. I know him better than you do. If he were
to find out we hadn't told him, he'd be angry. I know.
(*She takes off her glasses.*)

I

. . . Hello? Good morning. Could I please speak to Mr Salvatore Di Vita. I'm his mother . . .

2: ROME. STREETS. EXT/INT. NIGHT
It's late, but there is still traffic on the streets heading downtown. Inside a high-powered car, a man around fifty is driving. It is SALVATORE DI VITA. *Elegant, just growing grey, a handsome face creased by deep wrinkles. His weary expression hides the determined, self-assured manner of the successful self-made man. He must be a heavy smoker judging by the way he draws the last puffs on his cigarette.*
He stops at a red light. He stubs out the cigarette and rolls down the window, as a little Fiat Uno pulls up alongside. A rock tune plays full blast on the radio. SALVATORE *turns instinctively to have a look at the man at the wheel: a* BOY *with a brush cut standing straight in the latest fashion. He studies the* BOY's *expression with almost exaggerated attention, but devoid of curiosity, coldly. The* GIRL *sitting beside him, lots of curly hair, overripe red lips, returns* SALVATORE's *look, provocatively. The* BOY *notices, turns to* SALVATORE *in a surly voice:*
BOY: Hey! What the fuck you looking at!!?
> (*Green light. The Fiat Uno shoots off, leaving a trail of music in its wake.*)

3: ROME. SALVATORE'S APARTMENT. INT. NIGHT
The apartment is luxurious, tastefully furnished. There is no one waiting for SALVATORE. *Through the picture window on the terrace, the city can be seen slumbering in the night.* SALVATORE *gets undressed on his way to the bedroom. He moves quietly, as if to make no noise. He doesn't even turn on the light, finishes getting undressed in the pale blue glow coming from the picture window. A rustling sound, a movement on the bed, the voice of a woman waking up.*
CLARA: Salvatore . . . But what time is it?
> (*She turns on the bedside light. It is* CLARA, *a young woman around thirty.* SALVATORE *climbs in beside her under the covers, kisses her sweetly, then in a whisper:*)
SALVATORE: It's late, Clara. Sorry, but I wasn't able to let you know I wouldn't be coming . . .
> (*He fondles her, but he is tired, feels like sleeping.*)
> Go to sleep now. Sleep.

(*He turns over on the other side.* CLARA *shuts her eyes, is about to drop off, but whispers:*)

CLARA: Your mother phoned. She took me for somebody else . . .

SALVATORE: (*Surprised*) And what'd you tell her?

CLARA: I played dumb, so as not to disappoint her. We had a nice little talk. She says you never go see her, and when she wants to see you she has to come to Rome . . . Is it true?

(SALVATORE *doesn't answer. God only knows how often he's heard that question before.*)

SALVATORE: She phoned just to say that?

(*She reaches out to switch off the light, buries her head into the pillow.*)

CLARA: She said a certain Alfredo had died. And the funeral's taking place tomorrow afternoon . . .

(*A strange look suddenly comes into* SALVATORE's *eyes. The idea of going to sleep has clearly left him. It's a piece of news he didn't expect. That's taken him off-guard.* CLARA *would like to carry on the conversation, but sleepiness makes it almost impossible. All she can manage is one last question in a faint little voice:*)

Who is it? A relative of yours?

SALVATORE: No. Sleep. Go to sleep.

(*She falls asleep in the dead silence of the night.* SALVATORE *is seized by a sort of chill: a deep, troubled feeling. He gazes through the window at the city, with its shimmering lights still moving in the darkness, suddenly shrouded in a heavy curtain of rain. But he gazes off, beyond the row of houses, beyond the dark sky; the shadow of a wind chime plays across his face summoning up endless memories, drawing forth from the infinite depths of oblivion a past that he thought had vanished, been wiped out, and instead now re-emerges, comes back to life, takes on light, superimposing itself on the mellow middle-aged features of his face, in the shadow of the city shaken by the storm, until another image is formed, an ancient, remote image . . .*)

4: GIANCALDO. CHURCH AND SACRISTY. INT. MORNING
An image from over forty years before. In the baroque church of Giancaldo. SALVATORE *is nine years old. Dressed as an altar boy, he is kneeling by the altar with a little silver bell in his hands. The congregation is also kneeling. The* PRIEST *is consecrating the Host.*

3

Little SALVATORE *has just got out of bed, is still half-asleep, yawns and doesn't notice that the* PRIEST *is standing there with the Host in the air glaring at him, as if trying to tell him something.*
PRIEST: Pss! Pssst!
  (SALVATORE *finishes yawning and opening his eyes meets the withering look of the* PRIEST. *He gets the message at once and rings the bell. Now the* PRIEST *can carry on, lifts the chalice and the bell is heard again.*
  Cut to:
  The service is over. The PRIEST *is in the sacristy removing his vestments. And* SALVATORE *is also there, removing his altar-boy tunic.*)
PRIEST: But how can I make you understand? Without the bell I just can't go on! Always half asleep, you are! What do you do at night anyway? Eat instead of sleep?
SALVATORE: Father, at my house we don't even eat at noon. That's why I'm always sleepy. That's what the vet says.
  (*The* PRIEST *has finished disrobing. He takes the bell* SALVATORE *was holding during the service and turns to leave.*)
PRIEST: All right, Totò, get moving, I've got things to do. Say hello to your mother.
SALVATORE: Can I . . .
PRIEST: (*Interrupting him*) And don't ask if you can come . . . Because you can't!! Shoo, shoo, off with you!!
  (SALVATORE *gives a shrug and leaves. The* PRIEST *goes down a corridor, opens a door, another corridor, and finally a door leading to an outside courtyard. He cuts across it and disappears into another door.*)

5: CINEMA PARADISO AND PROJECTION BOOTH. INT. MORN-
ING
The PRIEST *enters a movie house. Not very big: 200 seats on the main floor and another seventy in the balcony. Along the walls, posters of films to be shown are stuck up between the light fixtures. In one corner, a statue of the Virgin Mary with flowers. The* CLEANING LADY *has finished work and is leaving. Up in the balcony, over the last row of seats, are the holes of the projection booth. The middle hole is camouflaged by the huge head of a roaring lion, all in plaster, and the lens of the projector can be glimpsed between its sharp teeth. There*

4

*there are two smaller holes, through which the figure of a man can be
made out, appearing and disappearing . . . It is* ALFREDO, *the
projectionist. He is around forty, skinny and bony with a tough
peasant face. He has finished loading the projector and is checking the
carbons in the arc lamp. Then he removes the glass from one of the
holes and looks down into the theatre, at the* PRIEST *who waves his
hand.*

PRIEST: OK, Alfredo, you can start!!

*(He sits down all by himself in the middle of the empty theatre.
Up in the booth,* ALFREDO *lights the arc lamp and sets the
projector going.*

*Down in the theatre, the light goes off and out of the lion's mouth
streams the glowing ray aimed at the screen. String music, sweet
and ominous, spreads through the theatre. On the screen appear
the credit titles of an American film of the 1940s. The* PRIEST
*screws up his face and holds the bell in his right hand resting on
the arm of his seat.*

*At the back of the theatre, behind the last row, a curtain moves,
opens a crack and* SALVATORE's *gaunt little face appears. He
has managed to sneak in somehow and stands there without a
word, spellbound, watching the 'movie' on the glowing screen.
The credit titles have long come and gone. The story is at a
turning-point. Up above, in the hole of the booth next to the lion,*
ALFREDO *watches the film, but his eyes keep looking down at the*
PRIEST, *who is now drumming the bell with his fingers. On the
screen, the male and female lead, two Hollywood stars, are in
close-up; the dialogue is passionate, romantic.* SALVATORE,
*carried away by those faces, by the way they talk, by the beauty
of the woman, slowly slips down the length of the curtain until he
is sitting on the floor, his eyes glued to the screen. The love scene
reaches a climax, the music crescendos, and the love-struck couple
finally fall into each other's arms and kiss. Instinctively, the*
PRIEST *raises the bell into the air, as in some age-old ceremony,
and gives it a loud ring . . .*

Up in the booth ALFREDO *hears the bell; it's the signal he's been
waiting for. He takes a slip of paper from a pad prepared for that
purpose and sticks it into the loops of the film containing that
specific scene as it winds on to the reel. The projection
continues . . .)*

5

. . . And also the kiss of the two actors. The PRIEST's *nervous look lingers on those black-and-white lips meeting and now pulling apart for one last declaration of love before separating.* SALVATORE *is wide-eyed, he's probably never seen a man and woman kiss before, it's a vision that for him has all the attraction of forbidden fruit, the horror of sin. The screen is now filled with the figure of a woman getting undressed, showing for one instant the white, voluptuous flesh of her broad, naked shoulders.* SALVATORE *stares in open-mouthed wonder. The* PRIEST, *in a fury, grabs the bell and shakes it for all he is worth. From the sound of the bell to another sound . . .)*

6: GIANCALDO. MAIN SQUARE. EXT. DAY
The tolling of the bell-tower rings out over the square. It is noon. The vast square, pale and dusty, is alive with people. A noisy line of men, women and cows waits in front of the fountain to get water. Pedlars hawk their wares in mournful cries. People come and go in front of the town hall. The working men's club is deserted. The entrance of the Cinema Paradiso is shut. Hanging outside is the poster of the film that has just been seen on screen. Up above, the windows of the projection booth are open. The hum of the projector can be heard and the loud, lofty music typical of 'THE END'. *Then dead silence. The showing is over.*

7: CINEMA PARADISO. PROJECTION BOOTH. INT. DAY
Despite the speed, numerous white streaks spin around on the reel, created by the slips of paper ALFREDO *has inserted into the loops. He is rewinding the film by hand on the film-winder. When he's not talking,* ALFREDO *usually sings to himself.* SALVATORE *stands beside him, taking in everything he does with those quick, thieving eyes of his.*
ALFREDO: (*Harshly, shouting*) You must not come here! How
    many times do I have to tell you?
    (*And he slows down the reels with his hand. The slips of paper
    are about to arrive. Here's the first.*)
    If the film catches fire, runt that you are, you'd go up in a
    burst of flame . . . whoosh! And turn into a piece of . . .
SALVATORE: (*Overlapping him*) . . . and turn into a piece of
    charcoal!!
    (*He's used to his terrorisms, pays no more attention. Not even his*

6

grim look scares him. Anyway, ALFREDO *catches the joke, starts to give him a slap, but instead reaches over and picks up a pair of scissors.)*

ALFREDO: *(Angrily)* Christ, that's a sassy little tongue you've got! Watch out, or someday I'll snip it off.

(And he snips a piece of film, pastes the ends together and goes on turning the handle. SALVATORE *picks up the strip of film and gives it a closer look. He sees a series of frames all alike with a man kissing a woman.)*

SALVATORE: Can I have it?

*(*ALFREDO *snatches it out of his hand, furiously, at the end of his string. He shouts:)*

ALFREDO: No!!! Are you deaf or something? I've got to put this back in when we wind up the film again! You're a real pain in the neck!

*(*SALVATORE *reaches into a basket full of strips of film. He takes out a handful: all kisses that have been cut.)*

SALVATORE: Then why didn't you put *these* back when you wound up the films again?

*(*ALFREDO *is caught out. He stops the film where another slip of paper is stuck in and cuts the scene:)*

ALFREDO: 'Cause sometimes you can't find the right place any more and so . . . well, actually . . . they stay here. *(Finding an excuse)* Besides, there are more kisses than you can count.

SALVATORE: *(Excited)* So I can have these?

*(*ALFREDO *explodes, flies off the handle. He grabs* SALVATORE *by the shoulders and shakes him.)*

ALFREDO: Look, Totò! Before I kick your ass all the way to China and back, let's make a deal. These strips here are yours, I give them to you. However! One: you're not to stick your nose in here any more. Two: I'll keep them for you, because you can't take them home for God forbid and save our souls, if they catch fire, all hell'll break loose! OK? Oh!!! And now scram!

(He takes him and turns him towards the stairs. For him the matter is closed. He returns to the film-winder. SALVATORE *sneaks back and while* ALFREDO'*s attention is elsewhere, snatches up a handful of movie frames scattered on the counter, stuffs them into his pocket and . . .)*

7

SALVATORE: What sort of deal is this? The strips are mine! So
   why can't I come see them?
   (*And he stares at* ALFREDO *with a sly, saucy look.* ALFREDO
   *clutches his hand, darts forth like an arrow and is about to give
   him a kick in the ass. He shrieks:*)
ALFREDO: Get out!! And don't show your face here again!
   (*And before the kick reaches its destination,* SALVATORE *has
   already dashed off down the spiral staircase.*)

8: GIANCALDO. SALVATORE'S HOUSE. INT. EVENING
That was not the first theft of film strips. SALVATORE'*s hand reaches
into a flowery metal box jammed full of pieces of film. He takes out a
few frames and holds them up against the kerosene lamp. Gazes at the
figures that remind him of the films seen at Cinema Paradiso, and in a
whisper mangles fragments of dialogue, the shooting of guns, the
musical climaxes . . .*
SALVATORE: Bang! Bang! Bang! Shoot first, think later! This is
   no job for weaklings! Treacherous dog!
   (*The house has no lights, is gloomy and cold.* SALVATORE'*s
   mother,* MARIA, *is leaning on the table in front of him. She is
   young, around thirty, and her pretty face is haggard, marred by
   all the sacrifices. She is sewing some clothes, is a seamstress.* LIA,
   *his four-year-old sister, is sleeping on a cot in one corner. The
   kerosene lamp projects the trembling shadow of the film strips on
   the wall, figures of prairies, gunslingers, thugs.* SALVATORE'*s
   voice changes, turns even tougher.*)
   Hey there, you lousy bastard, take your hands off that gold!
   You black-hearted pig, stay away from me, or I'll smash your
   face in! 'Ntantatàh!!! . . .
   (*In the heap of movie frames there are also several photographs.*
   SALVATORE *picks them up. Family keepsakes. A man in an
   army uniform. Then the same man with a girl beside him whose
   smiling face can be recognized as* MARIA. SALVATORE *takes a
   closer look at the man's face, then whispers to his mother:*)
   Ma, if the war's over, how come Daddy's never come back?
   (MARIA *looks up at him with a sweet smile.*)
MARIA: He'll be back, he'll be back . . . You'll see. One of these
   days . . .
   (*But there is not much conviction written on her face. She looks*

back down at her sewing. SALVATORE *goes on looking at the photos.*)

SALVATORE: I don't remember him any more – Ma, where's Russia?

MARIA: It takes years to get there. And years to come back . . . Now go to bed, Totò, it's late.

(SALVATORE *puts the photos back into the box and tucks the box under* LIA's *cot near the charcoal burner.*)

9: GRADE SCHOOL. COURTYARD. EXT. DAY

A noisy crowd of little children in black smocks, white collars and blue bows moves about the large courtyard where there are two tall palm trees. The boys head for one door, the girls towards the opposite one. The janitors line them up two by two, ready to enter. Here and there, parents and relatives accompany the younger ones. Beneath one of the palms, SALVATORE *pulls off the altar-boy tunic, stuffs it into the khaki-coloured cardboard schoolbag, takes out the smock and puts it on, as one of his schoolmates passes by. It is* MASINO, *and he's crying desperately because he doesn't want to go to school. His* FATHER *drags him along, yelling:*

MASINO'S FATHER: You can fool your mother but not me! Get yourself a damn diploma and become a policeman. You good-for-nothing!

MASINO: I don't want to go to school!

(*The sound of the bell. The black lines move up the steps towards the school.*)

10: FOURTH GRADE. INT. DAY

SALVATORE *is sitting at the front-row desk next to* PEPPINO, *a little freckle-faced boy. His attention, like that of the whole class, is concentrated on what is taking place at the blackboard. The* TEACHER *is standing there, watching a plump little boy, shy and not quite all there, do a two-figure multiplication : it is* NICOLA SCORSONE, *known as 'COLA'. He is red in the face, has one purple ear and one white one. He stares in terror at that '255×15' written on the blackboard. The* TEACHER *yells, waving a birch rod in her hand.*

TEACHER: Well then?! Five times five equals . . .?

(COLA *stops to think a moment, then . . .*)

COLA: Thirty!

9

(*The* TEACHER *grabs him by the purple ear and bashes his head against the numbers on the blackboard. A large thud echoes through the room, followed by a roar of laughter. The* TEACHER *slams her rod on the desk.*)

TEACHER: Silence!! (*Then to* COLA) The five times table. Dunce! One times five, five!!

(*The class repeats with the* TEACHER, *in a sing-song chorus:*)

TEACHER *and* CLASS: Two times five, ten! Three times five, fifteen! Four times five, twenty!

(*With a wave of the rod, the* TEACHER *silences the class, and finishes the sing-song with the fateful question.*)

TEACHER: Five times five?

COLA: (*Timidly*) Forty . . .?

(*Another blow of the head on the blackboard. Hubbub. Slapping of the rod on the desk.* SALVATORE *secretly shows* COLA *the picture of a Christmas tree on one page of the book, and mouths the word 'twenty-five'.* COLA *smiles, he has finally caught on.*)

TEACHER: I'm asking you for the last time, blockhead! Five times five equals . . .?

(COLA *turns to her with smiling eyes and answers blissfully:*)

COLA: Christmas!!

(SALVATORE *clutches his head in anger, watches the* TEACHER *flogging* COLA *on the back with the rod.* COLA *screams at every blow, and at every blow the laughter in the class grows louder.* SALVATORE *stares at the rod moving up and down rhythmically. But he is not thinking of the pain his schoolmate is feeling, but is drawn, rather, by that strange regular beat, finds it similar to another regular beat, that of . . .*)

11: CINEMA PARADISO. BALCONY AND MAIN FLOOR. INT. DAY

. . . *the rolling pin* ALFREDO *uses to flatten out a reel of film that has just been unloaded.* SALVATORE *carefully watches* ALFREDO's *every move. He is not in the projection booth, but up in the balcony, standing on top of the last row of seats. He peers through the hole next to the lion's head. His bright little eyes fix in his mind the things* ALFREDO *does, as he loads the film into the projector, shuts the fireproof housings, turns on the amplifier, checks the carbons in the* arc lamp, then lowers his head to have a look into the theatre and finds himself face to face with SALVATORE.

ALFREDO: (Sternly) What are you doing here?

SALVATORE: I bought a ticket. I've come to see the film.

(Meanwhile the USHER comes up behind him and grabs him by the collar, and he almost jumps out of his skin. ALFREDO laughs.)

USHER: (Yelling) Go sit downstairs! You good-for-nothing sponger!! (To the audience) Worse than rabbits they are!

(SALVATORE has run downstairs. The main floor is more crowded than the balcony, like every Sunday, and there is a great din. The BOY selling ice-cream, soda pop and candy shouts and runs around like a chicken with its head off. Now the lights dim, the hubbub dies down and the performance starts. Before the film there is a preview for Stagecoach. The screen fills with images of John Wayne, the pursuit of the stagecoach by hostile Indians etc . . .

SALVATORE is sitting in the front rows, right under the screen, next to BOCCIA, COLA, MASINO, PEPPINO and OTHER KIDS, all with their noses in the air. BOCCIA, the biggest show-off of the group, is smoking a cigarette. An OLD MAN appears through the entrance curtain, takes a couple of steps and shouts:)

FIRST OLD MAN: Hello, everybody!

AUDIENCE: (At once) Ssssssh!!! Sssssssh! Silence!

FIRST OLD MAN: Can't I say hello?

USHER: It's a double-feature today.

FIRST OLD MAN: I couldn't care less. I come here to sleep.

(All at once, a chorus of shouts and whistles fills the theatre. Up on the screen, a globe of the world appears, spinning among the stars, the logo announcing the newsreel.)

AUDIENCE: (Hooting and whistling) For Christ's sake! Cut it, Alfredoooo!

(The CHILDREN in the front rows also yell, but SALVATORE goes on being alert. He turns and looks up at the holes of the projection booth, as if it were an impregnable fortress. He watches the crazy dancing of light in the glowing stream that opens towards him in a cone. And besides, that lion's head, mysterious, almost gruesome, emphasizes the enigmatic secret of the movies. In his dreamy eyes, that lifeless lion seems to wake up with a ferocious roar.

SALVATORE *has a frightened look . . . Another lion roaring.*
But up on the screen. The MGM lion. The throng of children
imitate the famous growl all together, shaking their heads in
unison.)
CHILDREN: Grrrr! Grrrrr!
(*The film starts: it is Visconti's* La terra trema. SALVATORE *is in*
bliss. His wide eyes looking up at the magic square of light. The
title music. Another OLD MAN *enters at the back of the theatre,*
but before sitting down, says hello in a loud voice:)
SECOND OLD MAN: Greetings to one and all!
AUDIENCE: SSSSSH! Drop dead! Silence! Hey, kids, we're here
to see the film!
(*Now there is an important sequence. The audience is silent.*
Concentrated on the screen. BOCCIA *passes the lighted cigarette to*
SALVATORE. *He takes a puff and hands it on to the others*
without ever taking his eyes off the screen.
The beautiful star of the film appears on screen. A different kind
of attention takes hold of the excited audience. SALVATORE *and*
the others stare at her with open mouths . . . She leans towards the
leading man, a languid expression, their profiles touch. But all at
once, just at the best part, there is a sudden jolt. The kiss isn't
seen.)
AUDIENCE: (*Disappointed*) Ahhh! What a shame! I've been going
to the movies for twenty years and I never saw a kiss!
(SALVATORE *is the only one to laugh to himself. He knows what*
has happened.)
AUDIENCE: And when will we see one?
(*Up in the balcony, the audience is more sedate. The tickets cost*
more and the people are richer, more refined. Among them, a
MAN *with a moustache, the look of a public notary, is sitting right*
in front of the railing. Seriously, without batting an eye, he spits
down below with contempt. Right on the dot, a voice is heard,
followed by a chorus of protests:
VOICE *and* AUDIENCE: Bugger!!! Ssssh!!! Silence!!

12: SQUARE AND ENTRANCE OF CINEMA PARADISO. EXT.
NIGHT
The bell-tower rings midnight. The square is nearly deserted. Except
for a landowner near the refreshment stand, with a moustache and a

hat, DON VINCENZO *by name, who is picking out from a group of labourers the men he'll be needing in the country at dawn. He chooses, points his finger, calls . . .*
People come out of the movie house after the last showing.
The USHER *locks the front door as* ALFREDO *climbs down from the projection booth. Among the crowd there is only one kid,* SALVATORE. *Tired, half-asleep. He's seen all the showings. He starts to walk away when he catches sight of his mother standing on the opposite corner, wrapped in an old coat. She's waiting for him, in a temper.*
SALVATORE *drops his eyes to the ground, mortified. He knows what's coming. He goes over to her timidly, uncertain, gives her a questioning look.*

MARIA: I've been looking for you all day. Did you buy the milk?
SALVATORE: No . . .
MARIA: Then where's the money?
SALVATORE: Somebody stole it.
   (MARIA *gives him a slap.* SALVATORE *holds back the sobs, but his eyes brim with tears.* ALFREDO *and the* USHER *are nearby, have heard everything.*)
MARIA: What'd you do with the money? Go to the movies?
   (SALVATORE *nods his head and the sobs increase.* MARIA, *in despair, flies off the handle, slaps him again, but looks as if she doesn't really want to, as if deep down she forgives her son's escapade.* ALFREDO *catches on, speaks up on behalf of* SALVATORE.)
ALFREDO: Signora Maria, don't do that. He's just a kid. (*To* SALVATORE) And why are you telling fibs? (*To* MARIA) We let him in free. He must have lost the money inside the movie theatre . . .
   (SALVATORE *stares at him in amazement, goes on listening to him.*)
How much did you have?
SALVATORE: Fifty lire . . .
   (MARIA *wipes away his tears.*)
ALFREDO: (*To the* USHER) What you find tonight on the floor between the seats?
   (*The* USHER *reaches into his pockets, pulls out some odds and ends.*)
USHER: A comb, two heel-savers, a box of tobacco . . .

13

(ALFREDO *very skilfully reaches out with fifty lire he has taken from his pocket. And like a magician he draws the money out of the* USHER's *hand.*)

ALFREDO: . . . and fifty lire! (*To* MARIA) See?

(*He hands over the money under the* USHER's *astonished eyes.*)

MARIA: Thanks, Uncle Alfredo. Thanks. Good-night.

(*She walks away, dragging* SALVATORE *by the hand.* ALFREDO *gives him a wink.* SALVATORE *smiles and winks back, but he's not very good at it; he can't manage to shut only one eye. Everybody leaves and the square empties, as the* VILLAGE IDIOT *comes up to the group of labourers, beside* DON VINCENZO, *motioning them all to get moving.*)

IDIOT: It's midnight, I've got to shut down the square! Go away. The square's mine! The square's mine!!

13: CEMETERY ROAD AND VILLAGE ROAD. EXT. DAY

SALVATORE, *dressed as an altar boy, walks alongside the* PRIEST *who is wearing the ceremonial vestments. They are tired, have walked a long way. Behind them a donkey pulls a wagon containing a little white coffin and a bunch of flowers. Behind that a little procession: the parents and relatives of the dead child. The road is very wide, covered with white earth. The spring sun is dazzling. The funeral procession kicks up a cloud of dust that makes everything blurred and hazy, like a dream, rimmed around the horizon by the blue line of the sea. The procession now turns into the large gate of the cemetery.* ALFREDO, *working in the fields, takes his hat off and watches the coffin as it passes by.*

Cut to:

The funeral is over. The PRIEST *and* SALVATORE *are walking back to the village.* ALFREDO *appears out of the countryside on a bicycle with a hoe and other farm tools in the basket. He comes pedalling up beside them.*

ALFREDO: Good morning, father. It's hard on the feet, huh?

PRIEST: (*Breathless*) Yeah! . . . Getting there's downhill and all the saints help you. But coming back! The saints stand there watching you, that's all! God's will be done.

(SALVATORE *is about to open his mouth, wants to say something to* ALFREDO, *but he doesn't have time.* ALFREDO *pedals harder and rides off.*)

ALFREDO: OK, see you this evening!
> (SALVATORE *is crestfallen. He looks at the* PRIEST, *then at the bicycle riding away. His eyes light up: an idea! He suddenly yells:*)

SALVATORE: Ouch! Ouch! My foot!! I can't walk!
> (*He limps. Throws himself to the ground as if a snake had bitten him. The* PRIEST *leans over in alarm. Up ahead in the distance,* ALFREDO *turns around to look.*
> *Cut to:*
> (*There is a smile on* SALVATORE's *face. He is riding on the crossbar of* ALFREDO's *bicycle. On their way back to the village.*)

SALVATORE: Alfredo, did you know my father?

ALFREDO: Of course I knew your father. He was tall, thin, pleasant, and had a moustache like mine. Always smiling. He looked like Clark Gable.
> (*There's something* SALVATORE *wants to talk about, but he doesn't know how to start. He has a try with an innocent strategem.*)

SALVATORE: Alfredo, now that I'm older, I'm not saying I can start coming to the projection booth, to the movie house . . . But . . . maybe, why don't we become friends?
> (ALFREDO *knows exactly what the little rascal is up to, and answers in a strange, theatrical tone, as if he were repeating something he knows by heart, a remark taken from some old film.*)

ALFREDO: 'I choose my friends for their looks, and my enemies for their brains . . .' (*Laughs*) You're too smart to be my friend. Besides, as I always tell my kids, be careful to pick the right friends!

SALVATORE: (*Surprised*) But you don't have any kids!!!

ALFREDO: (*Spluttering*) All right, all right! When I've got kids that's what I'm telling them!
> (*The outlying houses of Giancaldo finally heave into sight.*)

14: SALVATORE'S HOUSE. EXT. DAY
LIA, SALVATORE's *kid sister, is crying outside the front door, terror-stricken. Her face is smeared with smoke and her little dress half-scorched and soaking wet.* MARIA *is distraught, damp with sweat, and tries to console her, hugging her in her arms.*

MARIA: Stop crying . . . The fire is out . . . I'm here . . . That'll do, that'll do . . .
(ALFREDO *and* SALVATORE *come up behind them.* SALVATORE *has barely leapt off the bicycle when his mother sails into him like a fury, shrieking:*)
Miserable boy! You're the ruin of me! Your sister would have been burnt alive if I hadn't been there! And all your fault!
(SALVATORE *darts off, chased by his mother, swift as a deer.* ALFREDO *doesn't understand what has happened, leans over* LIA, *who goes on bawling her eyes out, and sees on the ground, in the middle of the water, a flowery box all charred and still smoking, and all around scraps of film reduced to ashes and several singed photographs, the photos of* SALVATORE's *father.* ALFREDO *gets the message now, looks up at* MARIA, *who has caught* SALVATORE *and is dragging him home, hitting and slapping him all the way.* SALVATORE *covers his head with his hands to stave off the blows.* MARIA *turns to* ALFREDO, *in a stern, indignant voice:*)
But aren't you ashamed of yourself, Uncle Alfredo, playing with a little boy at your age?!
ALFREDO: (*Cowed*) But . . . what's it got to do with me? . . .
MARIA: And who gave him all those films? Promise you won't give him any more of this trash! Don't let him set foot any more in the movie house. The boy's crazy! Crazy! All he talks about is movies and Alfredo! Alfredo and movies!!
(ALFREDO *is crestfallen, didn't think that* SALVATORE's *craziness, his morbid passion for movies, could go this far.*)
ALFREDO: I give you my word, Donna Maria.
(MARIA *now turns one last time to her son.*)
MARIA: God's got to grant me one wish! Send your father back home! And he'll see you get what's coming to you!
(SALVATORE *lowers his hands, looks at her and with the dreadful sincerity of children:*)
SALVATORE: Daddy's not coming back . . . He's dead.
(*An icy flash runs through* MARIA's *eyes.*)
MARIA: It's not true! No! It's not true!!! I'll show you he's coming back!
(*And she beats him desperately, as if to enforce her stubborn*

16

hope, slap after slap. This time ALFREDO *doesn't step in, lets*
MARIA *give vent to her rage and fury, but* SALVATORE's *cries*
make him feel guilty.)

15: SQUARE AND PROJECTION BOOTH. EXT/INT. DAY
Another Sunday. A crowd of men has gathered in the square around
the café where there is a loudspeaker. They are listening to the running
commentary of the soccer games. They check their Sisal pools coupons.
NICOLO CAROSIO'S VOICE: . . . We're at the seventh minute of
   the second half. Turin is leading one to zero. The goal was
   scored by . . .
   (*The scene is seen from above, by* ALFREDO *who peers out of the*
   window of the projection booth. CAROSIO's *voice drowns out the*
   soundtrack of the film being shown. ALFREDO *is bored. He goes*
   over to the projector, looks through the hole . . . It's the last
   sequence of the film. The music swells to a climax as 'THE END'
   appears on the screen. Swift as ever, ALFREDO *turns on the lights*
   in the theatre, stops the projector. Looks back through the hole, to
   see . . .)

16: CINEMA PARADISO. INT/EXT. DAY
. . . *the house packed to the rafters. Voices and laughter of the*
children. Smoke, ice-cream, soft drinks. The USHER *has opened the*
emergency exits to let in air. He fights off the gate-crashers who are
trying to get in free. The sound of the sports commentary fills the
theatre. The village BLACKSMITH *is sleeping in his seat, his head*
thrown back and his mouth wide open. The KIDS *blow up the empty*
ice-cream sacks and pop them next to his ears. Bang! The
BLACKSMITH *wakes up with a start, in a sea of laughter. He yells:*
BLACKSMITH: Ah! I'll wring all your necks!! Or my good name
   means nothing!!! Lousy brats!
   (SALVATORE *doesn't laugh. He is sad. He turns and looks up at*
   the projection booth. He sees ALFREDO *through the lion's mouth.*
   ALFREDO *also catches sight of him.* SALVATORE *gives him a*
   timid wave of the hand, as if asking if he can come up a moment.
   The look on ALFREDO's *face is unmistakable, irrevocable: NO!*
   SALVATORE's *not surprised; after what happened it won't be*
   easy to win him over. Yet there must be some way. But what is it?
   As usual, SALVATORE *is smart as the devil when he's out to get*

17

*something. Through the emergency exit he sees a woman pass by
with a packet in her hand. It is* ALFREDO's WIFE, *and the
packet is his supper.* SALVATORE *leaps to his feet and runs out to
her.)*

SALVATORE: Signora Anna!

17: CINEMA PARADISO. PROJECTION ROOM AND SQUARE.
INT/EXT. DAY

ALFREDO *starts up the projector. It's time for the documentaries and
cartoons.* SALVATORE *peers in from the top of the stairs. He's scared of*
ALFREDO's *reaction, but pricks up his courage and shows him the
packet.* ALFREDO *sees him, is about to pounce on him . . .*

SALVATORE: (*On the defensive*) Your wife told me to bring you
    this.
    (*His expression betrays the 'put on'.* ALFREDO *sighs, realizes it's
    another one of his little games.*)

ALFREDO: (*Sternly*) Give it to me! . . .
    (*He takes the packet, unwraps it and lifts the lid, shuts it again
    and puts the container inside the lamp of the projector to keep it
    warm.* SALVATORE *hasn't missed a single gesture, but speaks
    with his eyes to the floor.*)

SALVATORE: I told my mother you weren't the one who gave me
    the films. That it wasn't your fault. But I thought you said
    the film could catch fire just to scare me. Now that I know, I
    won't steal any more from you. That's all I wanted to say.
    I'm going.
    (*He turns to leave but* ALFREDO *takes him by the shoulder and
    stops him.*)

ALFREDO: Totò, come here.
    (*All things considered, there is something in that little boy, maybe
    his feverish passion, that strikes him. He'll talk to him seriously,
    without resorting to terrorism, try to convince him. He lowers the
    volume of the monitor, sits down on the stool.* SALVATORE *raises
    his eyes from the floor and looks at him at last . . .*)

ALFREDO: Now listen to what I've got to say. I took up this
    profession when I was ten years old. In those days there
    weren't these modern machines. The films were silent. The
    projectors were run by hand, like this, with a crank. And you
    wound the crank all day long. It was really rough going!! If

you got tired and slowed down, boom! Everything would go up in flames!

SALVATORE: Then why don't you want to teach it to me too? Now that there's no more cranking, and it's easier?

ALFREDO: (*Firmly*) Because I don't want to, Totò! This is not a job for you. It's like being a slave. You're always alone. You see the same film over and over again, because you have nothing else to do. And you start talking to Greta Garbo and Tyrone Power like a nut! You work on holidays, on Christmas, on Easter. Only on Good Friday are you free. But if they hadn't put Jesus Christ on a cross . . . You'd work Good Fridays too!!

SALVATORE: Then why don't you change jobs?

(ALFREDO *sighs, irritated. He reaches out to turn the knob of the carbon rods. He gazes at* SALVATORE *as if he were a grown-up, somebody who's making things hard for him.*)

ALFREDO: Because I'm an idiot. How many other guys in town know how to be a projectionist? None! Only a jerk like me could do it. Besides I wasn't lucky. When I was a kid there was the war! When I grew up, another war! Now it's all different. Times have changed. And you want to be a dope like me? Huh? Answer me!

SALVATORE: No . . .

ALFREDO: Good for you, Totò. Good for you . . . I'm only saying this for your own good . . .

(*He gets up and, speaking all the while, goes into a closet with a bucket in it, the toilet of the booth. He turns his back and pees.*)
. . . Cooped up in here you die of heat in the summer and of cold in the winter. You breathe in smoke, gas fumes, and earn practically nothing.

(SALVATORE *listens to him, but taking advantage of the fact he can't be seen, he turns the knob of the carbon rods, just as he had seen done a moment before . . .*)

SALVATORE: (*In a loud voice*) But don't you like *anything* about what you do?

(SALVATORE *gazes at the photos on the wall: Keaton, Garbo, Snow White.* ALFREDO *smiles to himself. Sure, there's something about that damn job he likes:*)

ALFREDO: With time . . . you get used to it. Besides, when you hear from up here that there's a full house and that people are laughing, having fun . . . Then you're happy too.

(ALFREDO *is lost in thought, doesn't notice that the documentaries and cartoons have finished. The screen is blank. And down in the theatre laughter is not heard but an uproar of whistling and swearing.* SALVATORE's *eyes sparkle, he seizes the opportunity. He turns on the lights and stops the projector, just as* ALFREDO *would have done. At which* ALFREDO *buttons up his pants in a hurry and rushes over alarmed, but sees that everything is in order.* SALVATORE *looks at him all smiles, as if he expected a medal for civil bravery. Instead,* ALFREDO *reacts like a wild animal.*)

So I've been wasting my breath? You pretend to agree with me, but as soon as my back is turned, you do what you want!

(*He gives* SALVATORE *a kick in the ass, shrieking:*)

Get out of here! I don't want to lay eyes on you again! This is the last straw! Your mother's right, you're crazy!!

(*He pushes him towards the stairs.* SALVATORE *suddenly vanishes, scared out of his wits.* ALFREDO *talks to himself, in a fury:*)

But how'd he do it? The little bastard! By watching, he's learned! It's incredible!

(*He peers out of the window, yelling, as he sees* SALVATORE *running through the square.*)

I'm letting the box office know: you're not to set foot even into the theatre! There are no more tickets for you! And I'm also talking to Father Adelfio! You won't be an altar boy any more either!!! You little runt!

(SALVATORE *looks at him. Hates him. Yells something offensive:*)

SALVATORE: Alfredo, go fuck yourself!!!

(*But his words are drowned out by the sudden shouting of the people outside the café.*)

CROWD: Goal!!! Holy Mother of God!!!

(*A* MAN *in the crowd crumples to the ground. The others swarm around him, alarmed. They hold up his head. His face is pale. They check the coupon he is clutching in his hand. A voice rises like a siren from the crowd.*)

MAN: Ciccio Spaccafico's won the Sisal!!!!!

(*The yell can be heard . . .*)

20

18: CINEMA PARADISO. INT. DAY
*. . . inside the movie house. The audience murmurs. Somebody opens
an emergency exit . . .*
SPECTATOR'S VOICE: The Neapolitan's won the lottery!!! Let's
    go see, kids!!! Northerners are always lucky!
    (*The whole audience leaps up and heads for the exit. Pushing.
    Shouting. Laughing and joking.*)

19: SQUARE AND VILLAGE. EXT. MORNING
*Summer has come. The village has a different look. The pedlars sing
their monotonous refrains in the village streets. In one street, women
are busy canning tomatoes. In one corner of the square, the* SHEARER
*has finished clipping the donkey and is now shaving the hair of a row
of bare-chested* URCHINS *with nothing on but their underwear. Then
another* MAN *disinfects them by spraying them with the hand pumps
used to spray trees in the country. The* URCHINS *laugh. The* BILL-
POSTER *is hanging up the posters of a new film,* 'TODAY AT CINEMA
PARADISO'.

20: GRADE SCHOOL DINING HALL. INT. MORNING
*The fifth-grade exams. In the vast dining hall all the children are
seated, one for each desk, under the watchful eyes of the teachers.*
SALVATORE, BOCCIA, PEPPINO, MASINO *and* COLA *have taken
places here and there, as nervous as everybody else. The* EXAMINING
BOARD MEMBER *is dictating the text of the arithmetic problem.*
EXAMINING BOARD MEMBER: A merchant owns two stores. In
    the first he sells fruit and vegetables. In the second he sells
    nails and cement . . .
    (*The* PRINCIPAL *comes in, interrupts the dictation.*)
PRINCIPAL: Excuse me, professor. Here are the men taking the
    exam for the elementary school certificate. (*Turning to the
    door*) Come in, please . . .
    (*All the children turn to look. A* MAN *around thirty enters, ill at
    ease. The children recognize him and laugh mischievously. The
    second is the* BLACKSMITH, *the one who falls asleep at the
    movies. The third is a twenty-year-old-boy,* ANGELO. *The fourth
    is* ALFREDO, *embarrassed and red in the face.* SALVATORE *is
    speechless. Gives a slightly ironic laugh. There is a look of
    revenge in his shrewd little eyes.*)

21

Cut to:
*The assignment is now being carried out. There is dead silence in
the hall.* TEACHERS *and the* PRINCIPAL *move about, checking
to be sure there are no notes being handed around or other forms of
'collaboration'. The four outsiders are having a hard time. It can
be seen on their faces.* ALFREDO *is also in trouble, doesn't know
how to solve the problem, the calculations are too difficult. He
looks at the desk next to him, where* SALVATORE *is sitting.*
SALVATORE *is about to look up at him, but* ALFREDO
*immediately looks away, too proud to let himself be seen. The
exchange of glances continues, grotesque, almost comical.*
SALVATORE *meanwhile writes down numbers and operations
quite quickly.* ALFREDO *can't stand it any longer, is nervous,
beaded with sweat. He's sorry he ever showed up.* SALVATORE
laughs up his sleeve, now he has the upper hand. ALFREDO *tries
sneaking a look at his exercise book in order to copy something.
But* SALVATORE *turns his back, hiding it from sight.* ALFREDO
*tries sneaking a look at somebody else's exercise book, but the
damn kid also covers it. It looks like a conspiracy against him.*
ALFREDO *has no way out. He has to accept the idea of eating
humble pie. He looks at* SALVATORE, *motions him with his eyes
in a conversation of glances. He asks for help, but* SALVATORE
stands firm, implacable. ALFREDO *tries to put it into words in a
low voice.)*
ALFREDO: You jerk. Tell me how to solve this fucking problem!
TEACHER: Ssssh! Silence back there!!
    (ALFREDO *insists with his eyes.* SALVATORE *makes him
understand with gestures that he could help him maybe, but . . .
on one condition. He imitates the gesture of winding the crank of
the projector.* ALFREDO *gets the message. It's pure blackmail. He
rubs his hand over his sweating face, raises his eyes to the ceiling
as if he were swearing. Then he surrenders, accepts the condition.*
SALVATORE *is serious, does not flaunt his victory, but you can tell
he is happy. He takes out a sheet of paper he had already
prepared, with the solution to the problem, rolls it up into a tiny
ball and as soon as the* TEACHER *passes by, takes aim and flicks
it to him.* ALFREDO's *hand catches the precious and dearly
bought message in mid-air.*
Their quarrel is over.

A bright, lilting tune marks the rhythm of the quick, blurred images, as in a dance, the images of ALFREDO *teaching* SALVATORE *all the secrets of the projectionist trade.*

ALFREDO *slips the reel on to the projector, unrolls the trailer and hands it to* SALVATORE. SALVATORE *mounts the film on the sprockets.*

Now SALVATORE *sets the projector into motion, opens the shutter and stands on tip-toe to see the screen from the hole . . .*

A shot from In nome della legge. *The main-floor audience applauds a line spoken by Massimo Girotti. And from the balcony, the same little* MAN *with the face of a public notary spits below.*

MAIN FLOOR VOICE: Bastard!! Pencil-pusher!!

(ALFREDO *shows* SALVATORE *the running of the film. He points to a place on the projector.*)

ALFREDO: Pay attention. This is where it can easily catch fire. If it happens, the first thing you've got to do is break it off, here and here, so the whole reel doesn't go up in flames.

(*On the screen, a shot from* Riso amaro. *A kiss. Unrelenting, the* PRIEST *rings his bell.*)

SALVATORE *licks the film on one side, then on the other. He laughs.*)

ALFREDO: You understand which side the gelatine's on?

SALVATORE: It tastes wonderful!

(*A shot of Amedeo Nazzari in* La figlia del capitano. *A jump, an out-of-rack frame. The audience whistles.*)

AUDIENCE: Fraaaame!! Wake up, Alfredo!

(SALVATORE *tries to do a hand-binding.* ALFREDO *winds the film, hangs a slip on a nail in the wall.*)

ALFREDO: These are the shipping invoices for the film. They are always to be kept. You see?

SALVATORE: OK, Alfredo.

(*Down on the main floor, a scene from* Dr Jekyll *and* Mr Hyde. *Everyone screams and hides their faces when Hyde looks at the camera.*)

AUDIENCE: Holy Mother! What a face! So ugly!

(*One young man,* ANGELO, *doesn't hide his face. He looks up at a young woman,* ROSA, *in the balcony, who turns and smiles at him.*

(ALFREDO *gives* SALVATORE *a wooden stool. He's had it made*

23

especially for him, so he can be high enough to reach the reels of the projector and the arc lamp. SALVATORE *climbs up on it. He laughs, all excited.*)

ALFREDO: Now you can run it by yourself.

(SALVATORE *gives another smile. He is posing in a photographer's studio . He is all dressed up for first communion, holding a white lily. The flash goes off like lightning during a storm.*

Now SALVATORE *is posing next to his mother and little sister. They smile without budging. Another flash of light. Click!*)

22: FIFTH GRADE. INT. DAY

Another click. The transparency of Rita Hayworth in her black gown from Gilda. MASINO *is pasting it inside a minute pair of plastic field glasses. Other pupils crowd around him in excitement.*

MASINO: (*In a whisper*) Christ, what a piece of ass!!!

(*But there is not a cheerful atmosphere in the class – on the contrary, a strange silence. The pupils are all standing around the teacher's desk, having received their end-of-the-year report cards.* PEPPINO, *who shared* SALVATORE's *desk, is saying goodbye to his schoolmates.* BOCCIA, COLA, *the others. They have serious, sad expressions. He and* SALVATORE *kiss like grown-ups. The* TEACHER *is standing among them. One of the schoolmates does not respond to* PEPPINO's *goodbye gesture. He takes a few steps back, serious, scared, his eyes lowered.*)

TEACHER: Di Francesco, aren't you saying goodbye to your schoolmate?

(DI FRANCESCO *gives his head a little shake. The* TEACHER *leans over to him.*)

But why?

(DI FRANCESCO *whispers, almost into her ear.*)

DI FRANCESCO: My father says he's a Communist . . .

23: SQUARE AND PROJECTION BOOTH, CINEMA PARA-DISO. EXT/INT. DAY

Another farewell scene in the square. PEPPINO *to his grandparents. His father and mother are also there, saying goodbye to the old folks. There are tears. The cardboard suitcases tied with string are loaded on to the luggage rack of the black car.*

The scene is watched by SALVATORE *and* ALFREDO, *up in the window of the projection booth. They look like old friends. On the sound monitor, the strains of some American musical comedy tune.*

SALVATORE: Will they really find work in Germany?

ALFREDO: Who knows? . . . It's like an adventure. (*In a theatrical voice*) Hope springs eternal . . .

> (PEPPINO *from the distance gives one last wave at the window of the projection booth.* SALVATORE *waves back.*)

SALVATORE: Peppinoooo! Come back sooon!!! . . .

> (*The black car drives off, leaving a cloud of dust that envelops the suppressed sobs of the grandparents standing there waving handkerchiefs.* SALVATORE *watches the car drive off. He mumbles:*)

Good thing Germany's closer than Russia.

> (ALFREDO *rubs his hand through his hair.*)

24: CINEMA PARADISO. BALCONY AND BOOTH. INT. EVENING

The lion's head with the beam of light, seen from the balcony.
SALVATORE'*s face appears in the hole beside it, as he peers down at the images of the Settimana Incom newsreel.*

The audience is distracted. The snoring of a man sleeping can be heard. A pair of urchins pick up a cockroach with their hands, tip-toe down the aisle. The sleeping man is the same old BLACKSMITH, *with his head thrown back. A little hand drops the cockroach into the gaping mouth. The* URCHINS *take to their heels. The* BLACKSMITH *squirms, wakes up with a start. Spits, while everybody laughs. The newsreel is now about missing soldiers in Russia.*

COMMENTATOR: The Defence Minister has announced a new list of names of Italian soldiers, so far considered missing and now confirmed as dead. Families concerned will be notified directly by military authorities.

> (SALVATORE *pays careful attention, sees the black-and-white shots of the last war. The Russian campaign. The troops in the snow. Now in detail a heap of personal objects found on the corpses. Documents, clothing, glasses, photographs. One quick detail catches* SALVATORE'*s eye: among those photographs, for one instant he sees one he thinks he recognizes. He quickly sticks a slip of paper into the take-up reel, as when marking the kisses to be cut.*)

25

25: PREFECTURE. CITY. INT. DAY

The hands of an OFFICIAL *tear off several forms and give them to*
MARIA *who is sitting in front of the desk. She is dressed in black.*
SALVATORE *stands beside her, holding her hand. They have black*
bands on their arms. An empty stare in their eyes.
MARIA *is pale, a cold look in her sunken eyes. Her heart is bursting in*
her breast. And a lump in her throat prevents her from speaking. She
looks at her husband's belongings, identifies them: a gold chain, an ID
card and the photograph, the one SALVATORE *saw in the newsreel.*
MARIA *strokes it with her fingers.* SALVATORE *comes up and looks, as*
the OFFICIAL *concludes:*

OFFICIAL: . . . Unfortunately we don't know what war cemetery
    he's buried in . . . This is the form for the pension. If you'd
    like to sign it . . .

26: PREFECTURE AND CITY STREET. EXT. DAY

MARIA *walks through the city. She holds* SALVATORE *by the hand.*
SALVATORE *looks up, trying to catch her eye. He sees her crying, in*
silence. The heartbroken tears of someone who has lost the one last
hope, but held back, so as not to be seen by the child. SALVATORE
presses close and puts his arm around her waist. They turn the corner,
and walk off in the noisy city, disfigured by the ruins of war. A poster
for Gone with the Wind *catches* SALVATORE's *eye. He smiles.*

27: CINEMA PARADISO. BOX OFFICE. PROJECTION BOOTH.
SQUARE. INT/EXT. EVENING

Winter has returned. On the screen, a sequence from I pompieri di
Viggiù. *The theatre is jamfull. The sea of heads sways and shakes at*
the irresistible jokes of Totò. Some people have climbed up on the
window-sills. The aisles are crammed, all the way down to the screen,
where grown-ups and children sit on the floor, their noses in the air.
Some people munch crusts of bread they've brought along from home.
Almost everybody is smoking. A woman laughs, holding the baby she
is nursing. In one corner, at the end of one of the aisles jammed with
people standing, a girl laughs, but every now and then her expression
reveals a look of deep pleasure. Her body moves slightly. Clinging to
her from the rear is a man bathed in sweat. They are making love
standing there among the crowd, which notices nothing and goes on
laughing.

In the balcony ANGELO *is holding hands with* ROSA.
*The curtain over the entrance is open. People are also standing there,
seeing what they can from the distance, even a corner of the screen
through the forest of heads. But the line continues on outside . . . All the
way to the entrance of the movie house, out in the square. There are
crowds of people, shivering from the cold, who protest, shove, risk
provoking incidents. The* PRIEST, *Father Adelfio, is exhausted, tries to
calm them down.*

PRIEST: Don't shove! There's no room! For heaven's sake! I can't
give another showing, it's late!

VOICES IN CROWD: Father Adelfio, we've been here for an hour!
There are people inside who've seen it twice!!! Move on!!
Ouch!! My foot!!!
(*It has just stopped raining, the bell-tower rings eleven o'clock. On
the poster of the film a 'LAST DAY' sticker. The* PRIEST, *the*
TICKET-SELLER, *the* USHER *and* TWO CARABINIERES *push the
crowd back, close the front door. The protest grows louder. Fists
pound the door.*)

CROWD: Open up!!! Father Adelfio!!
(*The audience in the theatre hears the uproar. Reacts:*)

AUDIENCE: Ssssh! Sssssh! Be quiet out there!! What the hell!
(*From the window of the projection booth,* ALFREDO *and*
SALVATORE *look at the crowd down below, yelling and
complaining. Some of the people look up at them.*)

VOICES IN CROWD: Alfredooo! We want to get in! . . . Tomorrow
you're taking it off!
(ALFREDO *spreads his arms out as if to say there's nothing he can
do.*)

SALVATORE: Why can't we show the same film tomorrow?

ALFREDO: It's got to be sent to another town. And if we don't the
owner of that movie house gets pissed off.

SALVATORE: Too bad!
(*The crowd sways nervously. The* CARABINIERES *give order.*)

CARABINIERES: (*Exasperated*) Stop! Go home, all of you!
Otherwise somebody's going to end up in jail!! That's enough!

ALFREDO: (*Dramatically*) 'Joe! A mob doesn't think, doesn't know
what it's doing . . .'
(SALVATORE *gives him a curious, inquisitive look.* ALFREDO
smiles.)

27

Spencer Tracy said it in *Fury*. (*Mischievously*) What'd you
say if we let these poor devils see the film, Totò?
(SALVATORE *stares at him in amazement, all excited.*)
SALVATORE: Wonderful! But how can it be done?
(ALFREDO *turns away from the window. He gives a smirk,
imitates the tough American movie stars.*)
ALFREDO: You don't believe my words, but you'll have to believe
your own eyes! . . . And now get your ass off that damn stool,
boy!
(SALVATORE *laughs, eagerly, as if he were about to see a whole
new movie. He climbs off the stool. Both of them move towards
the projector . . .*)

28: PROJECTION BOOTH AND SQUARE. INT/EXT. EVENING
Trying not to put his hand in front of the lens, ALFREDO *removes the
frame with the glass that protects the projection. He wheels it around
and motions* SALVATORE *to look . . . On the wall behind the projector:
the film picture appears gradually, reflected by the glass, moves as the
glass moves all the way over to the window looking out over the square.
There it disappears.* SALVATORE *can barely believe his eyes, as if it
were a piece of magic. He takes a quick look through the hole to see if
the film is still showing on the screen. It is.*
ALFREDO: (*Mysteriously*) Go to the window, boy, and have a
look . . .
(SALVATORE *goes over to the window. Looks out. The reflected
beam of light ends up on the white row of houses facing the
square. It's like another screen. Except the images are
backwards, like when you look in a mirror. And here and there
are the windows of the houses . . . For* SALVATORE, *it's a
wonderful spectacle, like a dream, ravishing.*)
SALVATORE: Alfredo, it's beautiful.
(*A voice is heard in the crowd of people jammed around the
entrance to the movie house.*)
VOICE IN CROWD: (*Shouting*) Hey, look there!! The movie!!
(*All heads turn to look at the house behind them.*)
CROWD: Oh, praise the Lord!! It's true! Look! The movie!!
There's Totò!! Hurry! Hurry! . . . THANKS,
ALFREDOOOO!!
(*And everybody runs over to the other side of the square, in front*

of the strange new screen. ALFREDO *and* SALVATORE *watch with glittering eyes.* SALVATORE *lays his hand on the shoulder of his great pal.*)

SALVATORE: Good for you, Alfredo!

(*A close-up of Totò projected on the houses, and one of the windows opens. A* MAN *appears, in his pyjamas. Dazzled by the light, he shades his eyes with his hand. He sees all those people looking at him and laughing together.*)

CROWD: Shut the window!! Shut the window! Go to bed!!

(*The* MAN *is dazed. Doesn't know what's going on. Looks around, and sees the black-and-white figures of the film dancing around him. He pops back inside, slams the window shut, almost scared.*)

VOICES IN CROWD: (*To* ALFREDO) Sound!!! Sound!!! Alfredooooo!!

ALFREDO: What do you say, should we make them happy?

SALVATORE: (*Smiling*) Sure, sure!

(ALFREDO *takes the loudspeaker of the monitor, brings it over to the window, turns it around towards the square. He turns up the volume and the sound-track fills the square. A chorus of approval.*)

CROWD: Aaaaaaaa! At last!

ALFREDO: (*Looking at* SALVATORE) Do you want to go down there?

(SALVATORE *gives a contented nod.*)

Go on.

(SALVATORE *runs on.* ALFREDO *looks wistfully towards the huge image in the square.*

Down in the square SALVATORE *heads for the crowd, his eyes trained on the house-front screen. Behind him, the door of the movie house opens. The* PRIEST, *Father Adelfio, sees the film being projected on the house front, the people standing or sitting on the ground, laughing. His eyes nearly pop out of his head. Then he motions over the* TICKET-SELLER, *whispers something into his ear. The* TICKET-SELLER *strides over to the shivering spectators, pulls the pad of tickets out of his pocket.*)

TICKET-SELLER: Ladies and gentlemen! You have to buy tickets! Reduced rate!

(*An irresistible chorus of Bronx cheers washes over him.*

29

SALVATORE *looks around, highly amused.*)
CROWD: Fuck off!! The square belongs to everybody!
(The VILLAGE IDIOT *peers out of the crowd, all worked up.)*
VILLAGE IDIOT: No!!! The square's mine!!! Come on, kids, no
joking around here!!! Otherwise . . .
(The crowd roars with laughter. SALVATORE *laughs too, as if
carried away by it all. And over the general merriment looms the
shadow of* ALFREDO, *standing in the window of the projection
booth. All at once, on the house-front screen, the image of Totò
slows down for an instant, a white blister appears and spreads
until it fills the whole screen. The crowd gives a start of
bewilderment and fear.* SALVATORE *jerks his head around to
look at the booth.)*

29: PROJECTION BOOTH. INT. DAY
*The film bursts violently into flame among the gears and sprockets of
the projector.* ALFREDO *is taken off-guard. He breaks the film running
into the take-up reel, but is unable to do it for the delivery reel. He
grabs the film which is catching fire and pulls it out quickly, tries to
stop the flames from reaching the reel in the fireproof housing. A
desperate race against the speed of the fire. The flames on the floor burn
his legs.* ALFREDO *gives a jump, slows down the movement of his
hands for an instant and inevitably the flames run ahead, reach the
upper housing. It's like an explosion. The flames leap out, striking him
full in the face.* ALFREDO *doesn't have time to scream, struggles
desperately and falls to the floor. Meanwhile the flames envelop
everything.*

30: SQUARE. EXT. EVENING
The flash of the flames flares up in the windows of the projection booth.
SALVATORE *is appalled, elbows his way through the moving crowd.
Inside the movie house the murmuring of the audience can be heard,
growing louder and louder. A scream . . .*

31: CINEMA PARADISO. INT. EVENING
*A violent spurt of flames leaps out of the mouth of the plaster lion's
head, into the darkness broken by the screams of people rushing for the
exits.*

32: SQUARE AND CINEMA PARADISO ENTRANCE.
EXT. EVENING

The crowd streaks out of the movie house, enveloped in a cloud of black smoke.

CROWD: Heeeelp! Run for your lives!!!

> *(In the general panic,* SALVATORE *tries in vain to get inside, elbows his way towards the street with the stairs leading to the projection booth. The audience clashes against him, knocks him to the ground, almost trampling him underfoot. He is suddenly seized by a superhuman force; gets up, claws his way desperately ahead, with people falling on top of him and to the floor. He finally succeeds, starts up the stairs . . .)*

33: CINEMA PARADISO. STAIRS AND PROJECTION BOOTH.
INT. EVENING

The place is filled with smoke. The air is suffocating. SALVATORE *streaks up the stairs, gasping for breath. The projection booth is enveloped in flames.* ALFREDO's *body on the floor, burning.* SALVATORE *moves quickly, throws a blanket over his shoulders, drags him by the feet over to the stairs, as boxes and other objects fall on him. Using the same blanket, he stamps out the flames that have seared* ALFREDO's *clothes. With the force of desperation, he drags him further down the stairs which have been reached by the smoke but not by the flames.* ALFREDO *doesn't move, his face is burnt.* SALVATORE *looks at him and only now is panic-stricken, lets out a terrified shriek, like a wounded colt.*

SALVATORE: Alfredo! Heeeelp! Help!!!

34: CINEMA PARADISO. INT. EVENING

The plaster lion looks like a dragon spitting fire and smoke. The statue of the Virgin Mary is also in flames. And the movie screen.

35: SQUARE AND CINEMA PARADISO. EXT. EVENING

The fire has been put out. Nothing remains of the movie house but the skeleton. Everything has gone up in smoke. People stand around, dismayed. They gather around the PRIEST, *who is at once grieved and shocked, to express their solidarity and comfort.*

VOICES: What a pity! Poor Alfredo! What a terrible thing!! Cheer up, Father, is there something we can do?!

VILLAGE IDIOT: (*Laughing*) Burnt up . . . Burnt up.

PRIEST: What'll we do now! The town'll have to get along without movies! Who's got the money to rebuild it?
>(CICCIO SPACCAFICO, *the man who won the Sisal pools, comes up, dressed in style. He looks up at the charred cinema. It looks like a battlefield after an enemy attack. From the smoke and ashes to . . .*)

36: CINEMA PARADISO. EXT. EVENING
. . . The great lighted sign of the 'CINEMA PARADISO'. The movie house has been rebuilt. New façade. New billboards. There are people moving about the entrance. It is the evening of the inauguration . . .

37: CINEMA PARADISO. INT. EVENING
The lobby is crowded with people, authorities, special guests. There is the MAYOR, FATHER ADELFIO *and the new owner,* CICCIO SPACCAFICO, *dressed to the teeth. The* MAYOR *cuts the ribbon. Flashbulbs pop. Clapping.*

GUESTS: Cheers! Congratulations, Don Ciccio!
>(*The procession advances towards the stairs leading into the theatre.* FATHER ADELFIO, *with a nostalgic sigh, blesses the lobby, then the corridor. Lastly, the new auditorium, which resounds with toasts and cheers.*)

AUDIENCE: To the Cinema Paradiso!
>(*The* PRIEST *sprinkles the new seats, the walls, the screen with holy water . . .*)

38: CINEMA PARADISO. PROJECTION BOOTH. INT. EVENING
Now FATHER ADELFIO *is blessing the brand-new projection booth. He also blesses the new projectionist:* SALVATORE. *He is very nervous, but serious, self-possessed. His worried-looking mother is also there for the occasion. The* PRIEST *turns to* SPACCAFICO.

PRIEST: How'd you solve his being under age?

SPACCAFICO: I took out a licence as projectionist, thanks to friends down at the guild offices. But I don't know a thing about it. Officially, I do the job . . . (*Smiling at Salvatore*) . . . but Totò earns the money.

PRIEST: Fine. (*To* SALVATORE) Always be careful, my boy. Don't ever go to sleep. Be sure another accident doesn't happen.

Do everything poor Alfredo taught you. And may God bless
you.
(SALVATORE *nods his head seriously, assuming a responsible
expression. His mother kisses the* PRIEST*'s hand.*)
MARIA: Thanks, Father. Thanks.
SPACCAFICO: And now enough of this gloomy atmosphere. Life
goes on! I want to see you happy and smiling!

39: CINEMA PARADISO. INT. EVENING
*Laughter. The laughter of the large audience at the first showing of the
inauguration film. Among the spectators,* SALVATORE*'s mother,*
MARIA, *and his kid sister,* LIA. *Up on the screen, a man and a woman
kiss. The first time a kiss has been seen at the Cinema Paradiso. The
audience murmurs, surprised and excited.*
AUDIENCE: Ooooooh! They're kissing!! Look at that!! Christ,
that's news!!
(An OLD LADY *sitting next to the* MAYOR, *crosses herself,
flabbergasted.* CICCIO SPACCAFICO *chuckles. Rubs his
hands: these are going to be golden times for him.* FATHER
ADELFIO *gets up and stalks out of the theatre, indignant; he'll
never set foot in the place again. The love theme gets louder and
louder . . .*)

40: PROJECTION BOOTH. INT. EVENING
The same music spreads through the booth from the monitor.
SALVATORE *is by himself. He is watching the film through the hole but
strangely enough, the story doesn't absorb him.* ALFREDO*'s absence
makes him nervous, he gazes at the stool he used to sit on. It has been
repainted. A voice from the rear of the cabin:*
ANNA'S VOICE: Totò? . . .
(SALVATORE *turns and at the top of the stairs sees* SIGNORA
ANNA *and behind her,* ALFREDO, *her husband. He is wearing a
pair of dark glasses and walks with the help of a cane. He has
lost his sight, but not his spirit. He smiles:*)
ALFREDO: Any room for me in this Cinema Paradiso?
(SALVATORE *runs over and embraces him.*)
SALVATORE: Come in, Alfredo.
ANNA: (*To* SALVADORE) Totò, will you bring him home when you
close down?

SALVATORE: Yes. Signora Anna. (*To* ALFREDO) I'm glad you
came.
(*Cut to:*
ALFREDO *is now sitting there immobile. He listens to the sound-
track of the film.* SALVATORE *studies the way he stares into empty
space, and the idea of darkness frightens him. There is something
new in* ALFREDO's *manner, as if having grazed death and the
loss of his sight had endowed him with a deeper knowledge of men
and life.*)
ALFREDO: How's school?
SALVATORE: OK. OK. But now that I've got a job, I'll probably
stop going . . .
ALFREDO: Don't do that . . . Sooner or later you'll be left empty-
handed.
SALVATORE: Why? What do you mean?
ALFREDO: Totò, this isn't for you. For the moment, the Cinema
Paradiso needs you, and you need the Cinema Paradiso. But
it won't last . . . Some day you'll have other things to do,
more important things . . .
(*He reaches out and touches* SALVATORE's *face to 'feel' his
expression.*)
That's right, more important. I know it. Now that I've lost
my sight I see more. I see everything I didn't see before . . .
(*As* ALFREDO *moves his hand from* SALVATORE's *face, we see
that he is now a young man, and that* ALFREDO *is older, greyer.*)
And it's all thanks to you, who saved my life. And I'll never
forget it . . .
(SALVATORE *doesn't understand his strange words.* ALFREDO
can 'feel' he is troubled.)
And don't put on that look. I haven't gone off my head yet.
You want proof?
(*And he gives a joking smile.* SALVATORE *is curious, expects one
of his fiendish tricks.*)
SALVATORE: (*Smiling*) Yes. I want proof.
ALFREDO: For example, at this moment the film's out of focus.
Go see.
(SALVATORE *stands up in disbelief. He looks through the hole,
and indeed the film is out of focus. He puts it back into focus,
flabbergasted . . .*)

34

SALVATORE: It's true! But how'd you know, Alfredo?
ALFREDO: (*Smiling*) It's hard to explain, Totò . . .

41: CAFÉ IN THE SQUARE. INT/EXT. MORNING
As the BILL-POSTER *attaches to the café door a poster of* Catene – *the coming attraction at the Cinema Paradiso* – CICCIO SPACCAFICO *is speaking on the phone in the phone booth. He is clearly peeved.*
SPACCAFICO: Only two days? Are you joking?! . . . What do I care
    if all the copies are reserved? . . . *Catene* for only two days in
    a place like this! Why, people'll eat me alive! . . .
    (*Standing beside him listening is* SALVATORE. *He is carrying
    school books under his arm. In the café, several curious*
    ONLOOKERS *laugh as through the café window they watch some
    unemployed* PEASANT MEN *dancing together at the club.*
    SPACCAFICO *listens nervously, then shrieks as if he were about to
    eat the phone.*)
    . . . I know, I know. But even if I start showing at eight in
    the morning it wouldn't be enough! This is a big town now
    and you people at the Titanus know it perfectly well! I'm
    your sole agent and if I get pissed off I'll write straight to
    Lombardo, in Rome!! I'll give you guys a good run-around!!
    If I get my dander up, I can let fly, if my name's Spaccafico!!
    (*Cut to:*
    SPACCAFICO AND SALVATORE *are now outside the café, head
    towards the square. In front of the movie house, the*
    CHARWOMAN *is at work.* SPACCAFICO *is so nervous he lights
    two cigarettes without noticing it.* SALVATORE *is turning
    something over in his mind.*)
SALVATORE: Don Ciccio, I've got an idea . . . You remember that
    old abandoned movie house where they're supposed to build
    those low-rent houses?
SPACCAFICO: So what's that got to do with it?
SALVATORE: The projector's all rusty, but I could fix it in two or
    three days. Give the place a good cleaning, put in some seats
    and bring in a projectionist and we'll show *Catene* in two
    houses.
SPACCAFICO: (*Shrieking*) What the fuck you talking about? You
    getting into the act too, Totò? Titanus has trouble giving me
    even one copy and I have to say thanks! If I ask for two, the

35

least they'll do is cut off my head and play ball with it!
(*A shrewd look glitters in* SALVATORE'*s eyes. He smiles.*)
SALVATORE: Who says we need two copies?

42: CINEMA PARADISO. INT. DAY
The house is jammed with people. Almost bursting at the seams. The last scenes of Catene *move across the screen. Tears stream down the faces of the men and women. The children are unusually silent. Even the* BLACKSMITH *is awake, indeed whispers ahead of time all the lines of Nazzari and Yvonne Sanson, knows them by heart. Among the crowd in the balcony there is* ALFREDO *and his wife, the* MAYOR, DON VINCENZO *the landowner, the schoolteachers. Now the music is loud, heart-rending. 'THE END' appears on screen. The lights go on. And there is a great din and uproar as one audience leaves and another arrives. The race for empty seats. Quarrels. The* CARABINIERES *help the* USHER *maintain order and persuade the people who want to see the film again to get up and leave.*
USHER: (*Exasperated*) That's enough now! You've seen it ten
        times! I need the seats! I wish you'd all get the galloping
        runs!
CARABINIERES: Easy! Easy! Through the emergency exits,
        quick! Stop the jabbering!!

43: CINEMA PARADISO. PROJECTION BOOTH. INT.
The end of the film slips through the sprockets. SALVATORE *switches off the motor. He is particularly fast in taking the reel out of the housing. And even faster in dropping it into the sack* BOCCIA *is holding open for him.*
SALVATORE: Now get running and bring me the first reel.
        Meanwhile I'll start showing the news!
BOCCIA: OK, Totò!

44: VILLAGE STREETS AND COUNTRYSIDE. EXT. DAY
BOCCIA *speeds like an arrow on his bicycle through the village streets. Tied to the parcel-rack is the sack containing the second part of* Catene. *He now turns off the main street and takes a short-cut down a country road. He pedals as fast as he can. Until he disappears into the distance, beyond the trees.*

45: ENTRANCE OLD ABANDONED MOVIE HOUSE. EXT. DAY
BOCCIA *finally reaches the old movie house, which has been more or less spruced up. Here too people are lined up in front of the posters of* Catene. CICCIO SPACCAFICO *is waiting impatiently on an outside staircase. He too is holding a sack, containing the first part of the film. The bicycle pulls up in front of him. The sacks are exchanged.*
SPACCAFICO: Quick! Give it to me! Here's the first part. Get
      moving!
      (BOCCIA *heads back to the Cinema Paradiso, to take the first part to* SALVATORE. SPACCAFICO *dashes up the stairs, and hands the sack to a* MAN *standing in the door, through which the bare projection booth can be seen, and the projector which* SALVATORE *has put back into working order.* SPACCAFICO *yells in excitement.*)
SPACCAFICO: Here you are! Quick, quick!! People are waiting!

46: OLD ABANDONED MOVIE HOUSE. INT. DAY
In fact, inside the old freezing cold movie house, the audience is grumbling. Everyone is wrapped in overcoats and woollen scarves and are sitting on chairs they've brought from home and wooden benches. The hum of the projector is heard at last. The lights go down. The grumbling subsides. The words 'PART TWO' appear on screen and then the images of the film.

47: VARIOUS COUNTRY ROADS AND VILLAGE STREETS. EXT.
DAY/SUNDOWN
Meanwhile BOCCIA *pedals his way swiftly through the countryside on his way to the* Cinema Paradiso . . .
Fade.
Now BOCCIA *is on his way back to the old movie house. To carry out another exchange of sacks containing the reels of film.*
Fade.
Another race back to Cinema Paradiso. BOCCIA *starts looking tired, his breath is short. And daylight starts fading into the colours of sundown.*
Fade.
The last fading light of sundown. BOCCIA *is pedalling once more back to the old movie house. With the same sack tied to the parcel-rack. He is exhausted. On his last legs. He slows down, then stops.*

48: CINEMA PARADISO. INT. EVENING

*The lights are still on. In the thick blanket of smoke, the crowd stirs
nervously. Shouting. Whistling.*

AUDIENCE: Hey, when's it starting!! We've got ploughing to do
in the morning!! Totò, get a move on!! Heeey!!

49: PROJECTION BOOTH. INT/EXT. EVENING

In the booth, the projector is turned off. SALVATORE *looks nervously
out of the window . . . at the square. But not a sign of* BOCCIA. *A*
CARABINIERE *peers in through one of the holes.*

CARABINIERE: What are we going to do, Totò? The whole place
here is up in arms. They've been waiting more than a half
hour.

SALVATORE: What can I do?

50: OLD ABANDONED MOVIE HOUSE. INT. EVENING

*Here too the audience is up in arms. They're waiting for Part Two to
start.* CICCIO SPACCAFICO *tears his hair with rage.*

SPACCAFICO: Where's the fucking bastard got to?

SPECTATOR: Let's get one thing straight, Don Ciccio! I'm waiting
ten minutes more, and if you haven't started . . . you're
giving me my money back!!

AUDIENCE: (*In chorus*) Well said! Well said! We want our money
back!!

SPACCAFICO: Easy! Easy! What about my showing you the first
part again? Huh?

(*People shout, whistle, give Bronx cheers.*)

AUDIENCE: Noo! First part, my foot! We want to see how the
story ends!!

(*Down in the front row,* PASQUALE, *the man who sells black-
market cigarettes, stands up.*)

PASQUALE: I've seen the whole works! You want me to tell you
how it ends?

(*A shoe comes flying at him.*)

AUDIENCE: Nooo! No! Shut up, you jerk!!

51: VILLAGE STREETS AND COUNTRY ROADS. EXT. EVENING

SALVATORE *has got himself a bicycle and is going off to look for*
BOCCIA. *He pedals fast, turns into the country short cut. Looks*

around: not a sign of Boccia. By now it is dark. He sees a MAN *in the window of a farmhouse, calls out to him.*

SALVATORE: Boccia! Boccia!

(SALVATORE *rides on. Now he's in the open country. All of a sudden he seems to hear something. He stops. Pricks up his ears. It's a sort of moan – he can't figure out if it's an animal or a man. He turns on the flashlight he has brought along. Takes a closer look around. Catches sight of a bicycle wheel on the ground behind a bush. That's where the moan is coming from! He creeps over in alarm. Next to the bicycle he now catches sight of the sack with the film. And the moaning gets louder.*)

SALVATORE: (*Alarmed*) Boccia, what's wrong?

(*He runs over to help his friend. Behind the bush he discovers* BOCCIA *humped up between the legs of* TERESA, *a prostitute. He moves with all the fury of his young years.* SALVATORE *has never seen people making love before and is speechless.*) Damn you, what are you doing?

BOCCIA: (*Shouting*) Oh, Christ, it's so good!!!

(*And he goes on ramming it home.*)

TERESA: Hey, cut it out! Go away. Shoo!

(*With a confused look on his face,* SALVATORE *picks up the sack and walks away, looking over his shoulder at the couple who go on tossing around more and more frantically.* BOCCIA *lets out a shriek of pleasure that rings through the countryside, as* SALVATORE *pedals off like a madman and disappears into the trees.*)

52: CINEMA PARADISO. INT. DAY/EVENING

Music and the naked body of Brigitte Bardot. A row of youngsters on the main floor stare at the naked actress, all excited. A regular rhythmic tremor runs through them, half-hidden by the back of the seats.

A scene from a horror film. The frightened faces of the audience. Off in one corner, the door of the men's toilet opens and a MAN *with a contented look comes out, followed by* TERESA, *who motions another one to come in.*

In the projection booth, SALVATORE *is eating the meal his mother has brought him.*

A gangster film. The tense faces of the audience. A gun battle. Rounds of machine-gun fire in the night. The shots echo through the theatre. A LITTLE BOY *claps his hands over his ears. Alternating with the machine-gun fire on screen, a real pistol shoots the back of one of the spectators, the landowner* DON VINCENZO, *who slumps down in his seat without anybody noticing . . . The shooting continues up on screen . . .*

SALVATORE'*s hand holds a lighted match under a piece of film, before the horrified eyes of* SPACCAFICO *and the* USHER, *and the puzzled expression of* ALFREDO.
SALVATORE: What'd I tell you? It doesn't catch fire!
ALFREDO: Progress! It always arrives too late!

A scene from Seven Brides for Seven Brothers. *The only empty seat in the theatre is the one where* DON VINCENZO *was killed. A flower has been tied to it with string. All the other seats are taken.*
Fade to:
ROSA *and* ANGELO *are sitting next to each other. They are watching a different film. But she has a baby in her arms: they have got married, have set up a family.*
In the balcony, the MAN *with the face of a public notary spits down below with a contented look. But this time the main floor takes its revenge and a blob of shit hits him square in the face.*

53: CINEMA PARADISO. INT. MORNING
In the morning the theatre is empty. All the doors are shut. Light filters in through the open windows up above, illuminates the posters of coming attractions and the yellowish screen. Off-screen, a woman's voice and a boy's voice are heard.
TERESA'S VOICE: (*Off-screen*) Come on . . . That's right . . . relax
. . . (*Laughing*) . . . Don't be scared . . .
SALVATORE'S VOICE: (*Off-screen*) Is it true that if I bleed I've got
to squeeze lemon juice on it?
TERESA'S VOICE: (*Off-screen*) (*A loud laugh*) Lemon juice? . . .
That's a new one for you! Who tells you this crap . . . Take it

easy . . . That's right . . . You see, it's not painful, is it?
(*Slow pan along the walls of the theatre, the empty aisles,
discovers* SALVATORE *on the floor between the seats with*
TERESA, *the prostitute who has already been seen.* SALVATORE *is
making love for the first time in his life. He is awkward and
clumsy. There is an uncertain look in his eyes, his livid face is
dripping with sweat.*)

TERESA: . . . There you are! That's right, that's right! Keep
going . . .
(SALVATORE *is quicker, has learned the lesson.* TERESA *goads
him on.*
Ah!!? There, now you're a real man! A *man*!? A real calf!
(SALVATORE's *panting slackens into a deep sigh of pleasure.*)

54: VARIOUS SETTINGS. INT/EXT. DAY
*The blade of a knife, clutched in a hardened hand. A blow. A cry of
pain. A calf falls like a dead weight to the ground . . .* SALVATORE
*photographs the animal in the throes of death with his 8mm movie
camera. As well as the faces of the* MEN *who now bleed and skin it
quickly. In the vast slaughter-house, the voices of the men and animals
mingle together.*

SALVATORE's *eye is quick to catch the most unexpected expressions of
ordinary people. His movie camera is always ready, like a hunter's
rifle. Now he is shooting . . .*

*A meeting in the square: the passionate reactions of the peasants
listening to a speaker who flails his arms around.*

At school: the old SCHOOLMISTRESS *sitting at her desk, sunk in God
knows what dreams, her eyes staring off into empty space, as a tear
runs down her pale, unhappy face, and the unknowing* STUDENTS
carry out their assignments.

*At the railroad station: the nervous excitement of the people waiting on
the platforms.* SALVATORE *pans his camera on to* TWO MEN *fighting.
But an arriving train comes in between.* SALVATORE *follows the train,
pans along the cars. The train stops. A door opens and the passengers
climb out. Several* TRADERS, *a* CARABINIERE, *a group of*

41

commuting STUDENTS, *the* TICKET-COLLECTOR, *a distinguished-looking* COUPLE *and lastly, a* GIRL *who stops in the middle of the viewfinder.* SALVATORE *is immediately attracted by her face. He goes on shooting without leaving it a moment. He follows her through the lens. She is very beautiful, must be around sixteen, a simple, sweet face, blue eyes. She is certainly the daughter of the distinguished-looking* COUPLE *who got off just before she did. The little family moves off down the platform.* SALVATORE *follows the girl's movements, as if hypnotized. Now she passes by him, turns towards him for one moment, as if trying to figure out where he is aiming that funny-looking gadget.* SALVATORE *smiles at her, entranced.*

55: HIGH SCHOOL. COURTYARD. ENTRANCE. EXT. MORNING
The JANITOR *is ringing the bell. In the courtyard, on the other side of the gate, the* STUDENTS *prepare to enter.* SALVATORE *is with a group of schoolmates, including* BOCCIA. *And they all stare, wide-eyed, at the* GIRL *from the station. She has her books under her arm and is walking by herself.*

SALVATORE: You know that one there?

BOCCIA: She's new. Not bad though. Nice-looking.

(SALVATORE *has the look of somebody seeking for an idea, some way of picking up a conversation with her.*)

SECOND STUDENT: Her father's the new bank director. Loaded, luxury and easy living!

FIRST STUDENT: People who jerk off with a shirt so they won't get their hands dirty. (*Laughs.*)

(*All at once,* BOCCIA *and* SALVATORE *notice that the* GIRL *drops her lunch without noticing as she is about to enter the school. They fly off, swift as arrows. It's a chance not to be missed.* BOCCIA *is the quicker, is already in the lead.* SALVATORE *gives an angry gesture. A flash come into his eyes, the same flash he had as a little boy when he finds the right way to hit home. He picks up his step, trips* BOCCIA *and brings him to the ground. He pounces on him and lets go with his fist. He starts running again. Picks the bundle off the ground. Catches up with the* GIRL *from the station, nervous and inexperienced, but polite.*)

SALVATORE: Look, you dropped this.

(*And he hands her her lunch with a smile. She recognizes him.*)

ELENA: Oh, thanks. I hadn't noticed . . .

42

(*She takes the bundle as* SALVATORE *touches her hand delicately.*)

SALVATORE: My name's Salvatore . . . And yours?

ELENA: (*Smiling*) Elena. My name's Elena.

    (SALVATORE *is very flustered. He feels as if all his blood were throbbing in his head. He tries to say something else, but the words catch in his throat.*)

SALVATORE: I . . . I . . . The other time at the station.

    (BOCCIA *suddenly grabs him by the collar and yanks him away.* ELENA *is frightened, puts her hand over her eyes so as not to see.*)

56: CINEMA PARADISO. PROJECTION BOOTH. INT. AFTERNOON

SALVATORE *has a black eye, swollen shut. He is setting up a little 8mm projector on a stool.* ALFREDO *is sitting in one corner. He has come to keep him company. He listens to the sound-track of the movie being shown.*

ALFRED: Chaplin's *Modern Times*! Right, Totò?

SALVATORE: That's right, *Modern Times*.

ALFREDO: I've shown it so many times I know it by heart. The first time I showed it, in 1940, was the Sunday my first wife died. They kept it hidden from me all day so they wouldn't have to close down the movie house. I only found out that night, after the last show. Those are things you never forget . . .(*Changing his tone.*) So, Totò, how are these home movies going?

    (SALVATORE *has switched on the little projector and a square of light appears on the wall beside* ALFREDO, *with the scenes shot in town.*)

SALVATORE: Yes.

    (*The shots of the slaughter-house have appeared.*)

ALFREDO: (*Whispering*) What is it, what is it? What's the picture?

SALVATORE: It's people in the slaughter-house killing a calf. There's blood all over the floor, like a lake. And through this lake another calf passes by on its way to die.

    (ALFREDO *is concentrated, as if* SALVATORE's *description transmitted the real image to him, the colours, the forms. The railway station has appeared on the wall, and the sequence of* ELENA. SALVATORE *does not move, does not say a word, as he gazes at those blue eyes looking into the camera.* ALFREDO *senses something funny in the boy's silence.*)

ALFREDO: Now what can you see?

SALVATORE: Nothing, there's nothing. It's all out of focus.

ALFREDO: (*Smiling*) Is there a woman? . . . Tell me the truth . . .

(SALVATORE *is shamed, uncertain, doesn't know what to say. A tender look filters through* ALFREDO's *dark glasses. He has obviously caught on and whispers:*)

There *is* a woman!

(SALVATORE *is forced to admit it, with a sigh.*)

SALVATORE: Yes, it's a girl I saw at the station.

ALFREDO: What's she like? What's she like? . . .

(*And as other shots of* ELENA *appear on the screen,* SALVATORE *describes her. As only somebody in love could.*)

SALVATORE: She's nice. My age . . . Slender, with long hair, brunette. She had big blue eyes, a simple expression and a little beauty mark on her lip, but really tiny. You can only see it close-up. And when she smiles . . . She makes you feel . . .

(*He stops. Only now does he realize that he has let himself be carried away by passion, by the desire to talk about her.* ALFREDO *smiles, spellbound . . .*)

ALFREDO: Eh! Love . . . what a mystery!

(SALVATORE *turns off the projector and heaves a deep sigh, almost of liberation.* ALFREDO's *sympathy does him a lot of good. It's nice to be understood. He moves over closer to him.* ALFREDO *runs his hand through his hair, whispers:*)

I understand you, Totò . . . The ones with blue eyes are the most beautiful. Whatever you do, you can't make friends with them.

(SALVATORE *is comforted by the way he talks. He didn't think it was possible to put into words the things he has felt since meeting* ELENA. *He nods his head.* ALFREDO *sighs.*)

Eh, there's nothing to be done about it! The heavier a man is, the deeper his footprints. And if he's in love, he suffers, because he knows he's up a one-way street. Because love is a meaningless thing when a man gets it into his head to do what he wants . . .

(SALVATORE *is touched by his sensitivity, by his intense, passionate, sweet way of speaking.*)

SALVATORE: What you say is wonderful! But sad . . .

ALFREDO: (*Smiling*) They're not my words. John Wayne said it in *Shepherd of the Hills*.

44

(SALVATORE *suddenly changes expression, as if discovering he was being made fun of.*)
SALVATORE: Stinking two-timer!!
(*And they burst out laughing.*)

57: CINEMA PARADISO AND VARIOUS STREETS. EXT. DAY
A grey, windy day. It is opening-time and the shutters of the movie house are being rolled up. SALVATORE *is about to enter through the small door of the spiral staircase, when in the distance he catches sight of . . .*
ELENA *crossing a street with her books under her arm. She is alone.*
SALVATORE *doesn't stop to think twice, dashes off, runs through streets full of dust, another square, turns the corner, but has lost sight of her. He looks around in all directions: there she is! He starts running again. And finally catches up with her, all out of breath, practically speechless with emotion.*
SALVATORE: Hi, Elena!
ELENA: Hi. Why are you running?
SALVATORE: No particular reason . . .
(*He is entranced by her eyes. He wants to tell her all sorts of things, say all the words he has memorized a thousand times. But now he can't get them out. His knees tremble. He does his best to overcome his confusion, but all that comes out is:*
Nice day, huh?
(*A gust of wind envelops them in a cloud of dust and a clap of thunder rends the air.* ELENA *laughs, amused by the blunder.*)
ELENA: Yes, nice day.
(SALVATORE *laughs too. He gazes at her long hair tossed by the wind. She turns to leave.*)
. . . I've got to go now. Bye-bye.
SALVATORE: Bye-bye, Elena.
(ELENA *walks away. And* SALVATORE *also turns to leave. Only now is he seized by disappointment, by regret at not having made the best of the opportunity. He talks to himself.*)
. . . What an idiot! What an idiot! 'Nice day'! Christ!!

58: SALVATORE'S BEDROOM. INT. DAY
SALVATORE *projects images of* ELENA *on his wall. He lies across his bed gazing at her image.*

45

SALVATORE: You probably don't believe me, but I'm going to become the leading man in your life. Sure, I don't look like Marlon Brando, but look at me, really look at me. Am I really so ugly? So should I try once more? Maybe I'll succeed. What do you say?
(ELENA *seems to be saying, 'Yes.' As* SALVATORE *kisses* ELENA, *her image disappears. He is left with his face against the wall in the white light from the projector.*)

59: PHONE BOOTH AND ELENA'S HOUSE. INT. DAY
SALVATORE *is in a phone booth. The telephone will certainly help him feel less nervous.*
SALVATORE: Hello, can I speak to Elena, please?
WOMAN'S VOICE: Yes.
(SALVATORE *recognizes* ELENA's *voice, changes his tone, turns sweeter, more personal.*)
SALVATORE: Is that you, Elena?
WOMAN'S VOICE: Yes . . .
SALVATORE: Oh, I'm sorry, I didn't recognize your voice. This is Salvatore, remember?
WOMAN'S VOICE: Yes . . .
(SALVATORE *finally speaks, says everything all in one breath, without stopping, without hesitating, in order to leave no room for shyness.*)
SALVATORE: Listen, I know that every time we see each other I make a fool of myself, but I'm not like that, I swear. It's just that when I see you, I feel shy, the right words don't come to me, I don't have the courage to say that all I do is think about you . . .
(*He has finally got it out. He's dripping with sweat, but happy at having succeeded. He continues.*)
That's right, Elena, you're the last thing I think of when I go to sleep and the first when I wake up in the morning. And at night I always dream of you. I know, it's not good on the phone. But please, don't get me wrong. Because I love you very much . . .
WOMAN'S VOICE: (*Interrupting him*) If you don't stop phoning her, I'm calling the police!
SALVATORE: (*Stunned*) But excuse me, who's speaking?

46

(*At* ELENA's *house, a* WOMAN *who is visibly in a state is speaking on the phone.*)

ELENA'S MOTHER: I'm Elena's mother, you filthy pig!

(SALVATORE *feels like dropping through the floor, tries to get a word in to explain, to apologize, but the flood of insults overwhelms him.*)

SALVATORE: I'm sorry, Signora, maybe there's a misunderstanding . . . I . . .

WOMAN'S VOICE: And don't call my daughter any more. Never!

(SALVATORE *has no choice but to hang up, disappointed, defeated. He's so mad he starts slapping himself.*)

60: ALFREDO'S HOUSE. EXT. AFTERNOON

Good Friday. ALFREDO *comes out of his house, leaning on* SALVATORE's *shoulder. They go off down the street, towards the church.* SALVATORE *has finished recounting his misadventure.*

ALFREDO: I told you, the blue-eyed ones are the most difficult.

SALVATORE: But why? There must be some way to make her understand!

ALFREDO: Don't think about it, Totò. Don't even try. With feelings, there's nothing to understand.

(SALVATORE *gives an angry gesture. This time* ALFREDO's *words do not quiet his frenzy, don't help him. He moves away from him a few steps.* ALFREDO *stands there motionless in the middle of the road.*)

SALVATORE: Stop it! I've had enough of your sermons! You act as if *you* created the world!

(*A bicycle streaks by* ALFREDO, *who gives a startled jump, as if it were about to run into him. He raises his voice, panic-stricken.*)

ALFREDO: Heeey! Totooooò! Don't get pissed off with me now! Come here! I don't know where the fuck I have to go!

(*A* MAN *on a bicycle almost collides with* ALFREDO. SALVATORE *fumes, goes over to him listlessly.* ALFREDO *puts his hand back on his shoulder and they start walking again.* ALFREDO *has calmed down, but his voice is determined.*)

And the next time be careful how you talk. Not to take credit away from the Lord, but if I had created the world, in all modesty, certain things would have come out better.

47

But unfortunately such was not the case.

SALVATORE: (*Laughing*) You see, it's like I say. You always have an answer for everything.

ALFREDO: I want to make you happy, Totò! I'm going to tell you a story.

(*And he squeezes* SALVATORE'*s shoulder. It's the signal for taking a rest. They sit in a doorway.* ALFREDO *starts telling his story, and his way of speaking is hypnotic, magical. With those eyes lost in empty space, it's as if his thoughts and his words came in from some other dimension, mysterious, hidden . . .*)
Once upon a time a king gave a feast and there were all the most beautiful princesses of the realm. Basta, one of the guards, saw the king's daughter: she was the loveliest of all ! And he immediately fell in love with her. But what could a poor soldier do compared with a king's daughter?! . . . One day he managed to meet her and told her he couldn't live without her. The princess was so struck by the depth of his feeling that she said to the soldier: 'If you will wait a hundred days and a hundred nights beneath my balcony, then in the end I'll be yours.' Christ, the soldier ran off there and waited! One day, two days, ten, twenty . . . Every night she looked out of her window, but he never budged. Come rain, wind, snow, never budged! The birds shat on him and the bees ate him alive! After ninety nights he was gaunt and pale and tears streamed from his eyes but he couldn't hold them back. He didn't even have the strength to sleep any more. The princess kept watch . . . And on the ninety-ninth night, the soldier got up, picked up his chair and left!

SALVATORE: No! You mean right at the end?

(SALVATORE *is amazed, dumbfounded; that ending has made a deep impression. They start walking again.*)

ALFREDO: That's right, Totò, right at the end? And don't ask me what it means. If you figure it out, let me know . . .

SALVATORE: I'll be damned!

61: CHURCH. INT. EVENING
Before the high altar, the Virgin Mary in tears clutches three spikes in her hand. And beside her is another statue: Christ descended from the

48

cross. MEN *and* WOMEN *stand in line to kiss Christ's wounds. Many people are sitting between the pews.* SALVATORE *helps* ALFREDO *take a seat, and at that moment catches sight at the far end of* ELENA *on her way to the confessional. She kneels down on one side, just as* FATHER ADELFIO *comes out of the middle booth and goes to the altar to say something to the sacristan.* SALVATORE'*s eyes light up. He has had a brainstorm. He leans over and whispers something into* ALFREDO'*s ear.* ALFREDO *nods his head.* SALVATORE *is so happy that he gives him a pat on the cheek, like a caress. Then he hurries over to the* PRIEST. *Says something in a low voice, gesticulates with some agitation, points to the pew where* ALFREDO *is sitting. The* PRIEST *tries to say he can't now, but* SALVATORE *insists, and wins. The* PRIEST *goes over to* ALFREDO, *leans over.*

PRIEST: What is it, Alfredo? Right now, of all times!

ALFREDO: (*In a grave voice*) Father Adelfio, I have a very serious
　　doubt that is torturing my soul. And you've got to help me,
　　because I've lost all peace of mind . . .
　　(SALVATORE *watches from a distance. He sees the* PRIEST *put
　　on an alarmed expression and then sit down beside* ALFREDO.
　　Everything's ready. He creeps over to the confessional.* ELENA *is
　　there, kneeling down waiting for the* PRIEST *to arrive. In an
　　instant, without anyone noticing,* SALVATORE *pops inside the
　　confessional. He shuts the little door below and draws the purple
　　curtain. On the other side of grille, only a few inches away, those
　　eyes that keep him awake all night.*)

ELENA: Father, I have sinned . . .

SALVATORE: (*In a low voice*) We'll talk about that later.

ELENA: (*Surprised*) But . . . who . . .

SALVATORE: (*Interrupting her*) Sssssh! Be quiet, pretend
　　everything's normal. I'm Salvatore.
　　(ELENA'*s eyes pop in amazement.*)

ELENA: What are you doing here?

Meanwhile ALFREDO *and the* PRIEST *continue their unusual and animated discussion. The* PRIEST *is appalled, crosses himself:*

PRIEST: But Alfredo, what you're saying is horrifying!

ALFREDO: I know. But take the miracle of the loaves and fishes,
　　for example! I think about it a lot . . . How is it possible
　　for . . .

In the confessional, the whispered conversation between SALVATORE *and* ELENA *continues.*

ELENA: (*Annoyed*) There was a terrible rumpus at home. My mother told my father. And how could you have mistaken my voice?!

(SALVATORE *is mortified, on tenterhooks, keeps an eye on* ALFREDO *and the* PRIEST *through a crack in the curtain.*)

SALVATORE: Forgive me, Elena. It was stupid of me. But I had to talk to you.

(*She looks up at him and her eyes are even more beautiful in the candlelight. This time* SALVATORE *finds the courage to speak to her calmly, with determination. That grille probably helps him, allows him to see without being seen.*)

SALVATORE: You're so beautiful, Elena . . . That's what I wanted to tell you. When I meet you, I can't put two words together because . . . you give me the shivers. I don't know what you do in these situations, what you're supposed to say. It's the first time. But I think I'm in love with you.

(ELENA *gazes through the grille at the two shining specks of his eyes. She is bewildered by that flood of passion. At that moment, an* OLD WOMAN *kneels down on the other side of the confessional and her face appears behind the grille.*)

OLD WOMAN: Father, I have sinned . . .

(SALVATORE *turns to her, instinctively.*)

SALVATORE: I absolve you in the name of the Father, the Son and the Holy Ghost. Go in peace, my daughter.

(*And he slams the panel shut in her face.* ELENA *is barely able to control her laughter.*)

When you laugh, you're even more beautiful.

(*She pulls herself together again and puts on a serious, but tender look.*)

ELENA: Salvatore, it's awfully sweet of you. And even though I don't know you, I like you. But . . . I'm not in love with you.

(*For* SALVATORE, *it's as if a knife had plunged straight into his heart. He sits there gazing into her eyes, at the beauty mark on her lip, without moving. Then through the crack sees* ALFREDO *and the* PRIEST *conversing nervously, God knows what they're saying. And he turns back to her.*)

SALVATORE: I don't care. I'll wait!

50

ELENA: For what?

SALVATORE: For you to fall in love with me too. Listen carefully.
Every night, when I get off work, I'll come and wait beneath
your window. Every night. When you change your mind,
open your window. That's all. I'll understand . . .
*(He smiles at her. She is upset by those exaggerated words, but
also intrigued.)*

The PRIEST *has meanwhile solved the problem that* ALFREDO *has
made up as an excuse.*

PRIEST: *(Exhausted)* You understand now? You see it clearly?

ALFREDO: *(Hypocritically)* Oh yes, father. Now everything's
clear.

PRIEST: And the next time don't go around saying such heresy.
You survived the fire at the movie house. But no one can save
you from the fire of Hell!

62: SQUARE AND ELENA'S HOUSE. EXT. NIGHT

Sweet poignant music accompanies SALVATORE'*s long waits beneath
the window of* ELENA'*s room . . .*

*A warm early summer night. The last spectators wander off into the
streets. The* VILLAGE IDIOT *makes his rounds of the square.*

SALVATORE *is beneath her window. He waits. The shutters are open,
but not the windows with the curtains.* ELENA *peers at him through a
dark crack . . .*

Fade to:

A rainy night. SALVATORE *is back there again. Determined,
headstrong. A dog keeps him company, taking shelter under an
overhanging roof. The window is shut . . .*

Fade to:

SALVATORE'*s hand adds another check to an endless row of checks on
the calendar. A check a day . . .*

Fade to:

Another night. Wind. The window is still shut. SALVATORE'*s eyes are
the eyes of a lovesick man prepared to face the hardest battles, just to
win, just to conquer his loved one. She peeks at him through the crack,
but he can't see her . . .*

Fade to:

The pages of the calendar are covered with checks. Several months

have gone by. SALVATORE *adds a check on the last page, on 30 December. Tomorrow night will be . . .*
New Year's Eve. The streets are empty. Loud merry voices can be heard coming from the houses. Old discarded objects hail down from balconies. Firecrackers explode here and there. SALVATORE *is there in the same old place, as usual. The shutters are open, but not the windows, and all is darkness inside.* SALVATORE *is wrapped in a large overcoat and stamps his feet to keep warm . . .*

63: SALVATORE'S HOUSE. GIANCALDO. INT. NIGHT
Toasts are being prepared in SALVATORE*'s house.* MARIA *is there with her daughter,* LIA, *then* ALFREDO *with his wife,* ANNA. SALVATORE *is the only one missing for the 'family' to be complete. The bottle of spumante and the Christmas cake are ready. The radio is on with the New Year's Eve programme.*
MARIA: (*Nervously*) But why hasn't Totò shown up? The movie house is closed at this hour!
　　(ALFREDO *has a know-all look. He tries to put her mind at rest.*)
ALFREDO: He had to do something for me . . .
　　(*Over the radio, music and merrymaking. . . .*)

64: ELENA'S HOUSE. EXT. NIGHT
More sounds of merrymaking, coming from ELENA*'s house.* SALVATORE *listens to it, sees the shadows of her parents and relatives, maybe even hers, ready to celebrate, welcome in the New Year. But further on, that window remains dark and shut.* SALVATORE *gazes at it again. There is a new look in his eyes, like a gleam of hope. Maybe it's the specialness of that night, maybe it's the fire crackers, the festive atmosphere, but something tells him that's going to be the right night. The night when she'll open her window. In fact, a light suddenly goes on in the room.* SALVATORE*'s eyes sparkle, have already taken on the hue of victory. The window is pulled open, and his heart starts pounding like a drum. The music reaches its climax. Two hands come out.* SALVATORE *shuts his eyes for a moment, to hold back the flood of feeling. He opens them again and sees . . .*
. . . The hands reach out and take hold of the shutters and pull them shut. The light goes out. It is midnight. An echoing voice does the count-down.

RADIO VOICE: Six, five, four, three, two, one, zero! Happy New
    Year! Happy New Year!
    (*And a roar of voices, shouts, explosions, fills the air.*
    SALVATORE *has remained standing there immobile, speechless.*
    Disappointed. Defeated.)

65: SALVATORE'S HOUSE. GIANCALDO. INT. NIGHT
At his house, glasses are about to be raised. There is a strange, tense
merriment. MARIA *is unable to conceal her concern, her presentiment.*
She glances at the door, hoping to see SALVATORE *appear.*
ALFREDO: (*To Maria*) There's nothing to worry about. He's
    probably with his friends. (*To all*) Let's toast!
EVERYBODY: (*Toasting*) Here's to you! Here's to you! Happy
    New Year!
MARIA: For Totò too, here's to you!! Happy New Year!!
    (*Everybody echoes* MARIA'*s toast . . .*)

66: ELENA'S HOUSE. EXT. NIGHT
But SALVATORE *is not happy in these first few minutes of the New*
Year. He feels hurt, humiliated, rejected. He walks off amidst the old
discarded objects flying down from the terraces. That was his last
night. He's not showing up beneath that balcony any more.

67: CINEMA PARADISO. PROJECTION BOOTH.
INT. AFTERNOON
Outside there is a violent thunderstorm. The pounding of the rain and
the rumbling of the thunder drown out the sound-track of the film being
shown. Two buckets are on the floor to catch the water dripping
through the roof. SALVATORE *is alone. For the first time he feels he*
hates the profession he's got into. He is tearing up the calendar where
he checked off the nights he spent waiting for ELENA. *He tears it into a*
thousand pieces, as if trying to wipe out the traces of his grief. He is so
absorbed in his thoughts that he doesn't notice that someone has
appeared at the top of the stairs and quietly entered the room. And now
stands there watching him in silence. The thunder is deafening. That
someone is ELENA. *She comes up behind him, realizes he is thinking*
about her. Whispers.
ELENA: Salvatore . . .
    (*Loud passionate music is heard on the monitor.* SALVATORE

*turns and sees her as if in a dream. It is a sudden blow to the
heart. The look on her face is wonderfully sweet, the look of
somebody who knows she is madly loved and who now realizes at
last that she is in love too. For* SALVATORE *it is an
overwhelming, almost unbearable moment . . .
A long passionate embrace that is never-ending. They are happy,
cling to each other never to leave each other again. They spin
around, end up against the wall where strips of film are hanging,
the first-part endings and the trailers. Another intense look, their
eyes locked . . . And it is their first kiss. A kiss at first timid,
hesitant, almost clumsy, and then becomes resolute, poignant.
Amidst the film strips dangling around and touching their young
faces.
Meanwhile the film has finished, the projector turns uselessly . . .
Down below the screen is blank, the audience whistles . . .
But* SALVATORE *hears nothing, neither the whistles nor the
useless whirring of the reels in the projector. All he hears is her
breathing, all he feels is the warmth of her skin.)*

68: VARIOUS SETTINGS. INT/EXT. DAY
The happiest, most vivid moments SALVATORE *and* ELENA *spend
together:
A country outing. They eat a lavish salad using the flat branches of the
prickly pear for plates.
A chase through an endless field of wheat.
In the projection booth. A cake with seventeen lighted candles.*
SALVATORE *and* ELENA *blow them out together. And then a kiss.*

69: ROAD AT THE EDGE OF TOWN. EXT. DAY
SALVATORE *is driving an old beaten-up Balilla he bought from a
car-wrecker.* ELENA *sits beside him, having the time of her life. They
roar with laughter. The car jolts, moves by fits and starts, jarred by the
holes in the road, and besides* SALVATORE *is not such a hot driver. She
fondles him.*

ELENA: (*Ironically*) You have a great future as a driver. If they
    don't arrest you first!!

SALVATORE: That's nothing to do with it, it's the car that's still
    being run in . . .
    (*He has barely finished the last sentence when the car gives a*

54

sudden violent shudder. A sharp report. A cloud of white smoke issues from the motor. And the Balilla stops dead in its tracks. ELENA *and* SALVATORE *cannot smother their wild laughter. They embrace.*)

ELENA: So now how do we get home?

(*Cut to:*

The two of them are standing beside the empty road, looking bored, as they have already been waiting a long time for someone to go by, a car, a wagon. When all at once a car comes around the bend, heading for town. SALVATORE *and* ELENA *flag it down. The* DRIVER *slows down. The back door opens, a* MAN *gets out. An alarmed and startled look comes over* ELENA's *face: that man is her* FATHER. *She sees him stride over in a rage. He has almost reached* SALVATORE, *who tries to be polite, to make the best of the situation.*)

SALVATORE: Hello, Dr Mendola . . . Hem . . .

(ELENA *buries her face in her hands, so as not to see . . .*)

70: CINEMA PARADISO. INT. EVENING

SALVATORE *has a bruise on his cheek and two Band-aids on his face. He got himself a good thrashing, and then some. The house is jammed, as on the great occasions. Curiosity is written all over the faces of the audience. But what they're seeing is not a film, but an instalment of* Double or Nothing. SALVATORE *is standing by a teleprojector which has been set up in the central aisle of the balcony. It is a machine that makes it possible to project television show on the screen.* ALFREDO *is sitting beside him.*

ALFREDO: (*In a low voice*) Totò, are you pulling my leg or something? How is it possible to see this television without film?

SALVATORE: Just so, Alfredo. There isn't any. And if you buy a television set, you can watch it at home, without any fuss . . .

ALFREDO: (*Sceptically*) Could be . . . But I don't like this business. It smells fishy to me.

(ELENA *is sitting in one corner of the balcony with her parents. Sitting beside her* FATHER *is the owner of the movie house,* SPACCAFICO, *who thanks him.*)

SPACCAFICO: (*In a low voice*) You see what a bright idea, Dr Mendola? But without the bank loan how could I have

55

bought the machine? If we don't get organized around here, in this day and age, we'll meet the same end as the Punch and Judy shows!

(ELENA *is not very interested in the TV show. She sneaks a look at* SALVATORE. *From the looks on their faces, it is clear that things are not going very well. He gives her a nod, as if to say he wants to speak to her and that she should figure out some way!* ELENA *leans over to her* MOTHER, *whispers something into her ear.*)

71: CINEMA PARADISO. TOILET. INT. EVENING

ELENA's MOTHER *stands waiting in front of the women's toilet, gazing at Mike Bongiorno emceeing the TV show in the distance. Inside the toilet,* ELENA *is standing on the toilet seat whispering to* SALVATORE, *who is standing on the toilet seat of the men's toilet. Their eyes are barely able to peek over the flush tank which they have uncovered.* ELENA *is worried.*

SALVATORE: Could it be your father doesn't like the work I do
    . . . That my family's too poor . . . Is that it?
    (*She gives a nod of the head, but only faintly, so as not to wound his vulnerability.* SALVATORE *sighs.*)

ELENA'S MOTHER: (*Off-screen*) Elena!

ELENA: All right!! (*To Salvatore, in a whisper*) For the moment it's impossible to see each other . . . As soon as school is out, we're going to go stay with friends in Tuscany. We'll be there all summer . . . Maybe if you came up, we could meet in secret . . .

SALVATORE: (*Crestfallen*) But we're opening the outdoor movie theatre this summer. What will I do all this time without seeing you?!

ELENA: I'll write to you every day. Don't worry. I love you. The summer'll be over and I'll be back . . .
    (*They reach out to kiss each other. Who knows when they'll be able to see each other again?*)

ELENA'S MOTHER: (*Off-screen*) Elena!
    (ELENA *climbs down, pulls the chain and walks off, leaving* SALVATORE *standing there on the toilet seat.*)

72: STREET AND SQUARE. EXT. DAY

Summer has come. A bevy of barefoot children chase after the carts carrying the carters' families to the beach to go swimming.

SALVATORE, *helped by the* USHER, *has finished loading the disassembled projector on to a wagon in order to carry it to the outdoor movie house. The* USHER *has hung a sign on the Cinema Paradiso to the effect that 'Showings to continue at the Imperia Arena', and now climbs into the wagon. The horse moves off slowly and the monotonous clatter of its hoofs reminds* SALVATORE *that the summer is going to be long this year, longer than ever. And he leans on the projector that totters and lurches from the jolting of the wheels. A cart carrying a cheerful and noisy family pulls up alongside the wagon. There are the* MEN *from the slaughter-house. They recognize* SALVATORE.

SLAUGHTER-HOUSE MAN: Well, look who's here!! Cecil B. De Mille! Hey, Totò!! When are you coming to shoot another film?!?

> (*And they laugh, with their gaping toothless mouths.* SALVATORE *doesn't feel like joking, not even like answering. He looks away, so as not to see their leers. He wants to be by himself.*)

73: BEACH AND IMPERIA ARENA. EXT. DAY

The beach is almost deserted, dotted here and there with groups of bathers. The carts and horses are scattered in the sand, near the Imperia Arena, where some WORKMEN *are putting on the finishing touches for the new opening. The wagon arrives and* SALVATORE *and the* USHER *unload the projector.*

74: BEACH. IMPERIA ARENA. PROJECTION BOOTH. EXT. EVENING

A sultry evening. The jacklights of the octopus fishers twinkle on the dark horizon. The sound-track of a comic film reverberates over the sea, the laughter of the audience mingles with the sound of the shallow waves breaking on the rocks. A group of LITTLE BOYS *in a boat pulls away from shore. They join some more boats standing still in the water, all of them crammed with* LITTLE BOYS *all looking in the same direction . . . towards the screen of the open-air movie at the water's edge. There is a funny scene.*

LITTLE BOYS: All seats are sold out! Free entrance and payment on the way out!! Sssssh!!

(And they guffaw noisily. Their laughter is echoed by more laughter, in the distance . . .
. . . the laughter of the Arena audience, scattered among the metal chairs. By dint of laughing, the people in one of the rows of chairs tip over backwards. Screams, laughs, whistles.
The projection booth has a door at the back with stairs leading down to the rocks. SALVATORE *is sitting on the ground, barechested, tired and sticky with sweat. He is reading a letter from* ELENA. *He is so engrossed the words can almost be read on his face.)*

ELENA'S VOICE: *(Off-screen)* Salvatore, my darling, here the days never end. I find your name everywhere: if I read a book, do a crossword puzzle, thumb through a newspaper . . . You're always before my eyes. Today I've got some rather bad news. At the end of October we're moving to the city where I'll attend the University. It'll be hard to see each other every day. But don't worry, whenever I can get away I'll always come running to you, to the Cinema Paradiso.

(On the Arena screen, with its potted plants and palm trees, a very funny scene is being shown. The audience again bursts into wild laughter.
And the audience of LITTLE BOYS *in the boats also laugh. One of them, laughing himself to tears, loses his balance and falls into the water. The others howl with laughter. A voice rises up out of the carousel of boats.)*

URCHIN: Fuck me! I've caught an octopus! An oooooctopus!
(Fade.)

75: VARIOUS SETTINGS. INT/EXT. DAY
The August sun is blazing hot. People are forced to stay inside when the sirocco blows. The streets are empty. And there is a strange silence. Nothing can be heard except far in the distance, from somewhere in the country, the love song of some carter . . .
SALVATORE *hears it too, stretched out on the floor of his room, his eyes fixed on the ceilng where flies buzz around nervously.*
The MAILMAN *comes down the street on his bicycle, rides up to* SALVATORE *and hands him a letter . . .*
Sitting in the shade of a white wall, SALVATORE *reads the letter.*

Next to him, the dog that kept him company at night, beneath
ELENA's *window. He gazes up at him as if looking for news of her.*

76: ARENA IMPERIA. PROJECTION BOOTH.
EXT/INT. EVENING
The Arena is crowded with sun-burnt faces. On screen, scenes from
Ulysses.
On a shelf in the projection booth, there is an enormous pack of letters.
SALVATORE *is worn out. The waiting has destroyed him. He looks*
like a madman. As he winds up one of the parts of the film, he repeats
her name obsessively, under his breath.
SALVATORE: Elena . . . Elena . . . Elena . . .
(*Now he is sitting outside on the back steps, a few yards from the*
sea. There is a breeze this evening, the waves are rather high and
the boats of 'gate-crashers' can be seen out in the water, rolling
fitfully but not dangerously. SALVATORE *stretches out, gazes up*
at the inky sky and talks to himself, just like a madman,
whispering:)
SALVATORE: When will this shitty summer be over? (*Half-*
shutting his eyes) In a film it'd already be finished . . .
(*Smiling*) . . . Fade-out and cut to a nice thunderstorm!!!
Huh? that'd be perfect!
(*A clap of thunder explodes in the air. Loud, rumbling.*
SALVATORE's *eyes pop open.*
The Arena audience looks up in alarm at the sky . . .
The 'gate-crashers' in the boats also look up and see a streak of
lightning ushering in another clap of thunder. One of those storms
is building up that ruins late summer nights.
SALVATORE *gives a contented smile as the cloudburst pours down*
violently, suddenly . . .
The Arena audience scatters with a howl and scurries over to the
overhanging roofs of the projection booth, to take shelter and to go
on watching the film despite the rain . . .
The LITTLE BOYS *in the boats quickly pull tarpaulins over their*
heads . . .
But SALVATORE *does not get up. He lets the rain fall on him,*
goes on laughing, incredulous and stunned as if a real miracle had
taken place. And as he shuts his eyes and lifts his head up, to
catch more rain on his face, and gives himself up to that

marvellous feeling of joy, a mouth comes to rest passionately on his lips: it is ELENA. SALVATORE *opens his eyes in utter amazement, it seems like a vision, another hallucination created by the rain . . . Instead no, it is really her!*)

SALVATORE: Elena! . . . But when . . .

ELENA: I got back today. You can't imagine the excuses I had to make up to be here . . .

(SALVATORE's *lips interrupt her. It is an intense, a stupendous kiss. They've probably never been so happy as they are at that moment. They cling to each other as the rain goes on streaming over their bodies, mingling her hair with his, binding them ever closer.*)

77: CINEMA PARADISO. ENTRANCE. EXT. DAY
Autumn has arrived. In the streets, the PEASANTS *prepare the barrels for preserving the grape must.* ALFREDO *is sitting in front of the Cinema Paradiso with* SPACCAFICO *and the* USHER. *It is a quiet moment, they chat, while the humming of the projector and the sound-track of the film can be heard through the window of the booth. The* MAILMAN *stops and hands* SPACCAFICO *a folded sheet of paper.*

MAILMAN: Don Ciccio, this is for Totò. Give it him . . .

(*And he pedals off on his bicycle.*)

ALFREDO: What is it?

(SPACCAFICO *unfolds it, reads it, claps his hands on his head, in alarm.*)

SPACCAFICO: Holy blood of Judas! Now what am I going to do??!

78: UNIVERSITY. EXT. DAY
ELENA *is waiting near the University. She paces nervously back and forth. Glances at her watch. He's late. She looks around in all directions and sees him at last. He comes running up to her. They embrace . . .*

ELENA: So what'd they say?

SALVATORE: The army says that, as a war orphan, I don't have to serve in the Military, but nothing can be done. It's a bureaucratic error. I have to leave. Day after tomorrow morning. They're sending me to Rome. But they'll discharge me ten days later. Let's go . . .

(*He takes her hand, turns to go to a café.* ELENA *holds back. She has caught sight of her* FATHER's *car approaching.* ELENA *turns to look and in a faint voice reveals the reason for her nervousness.*)

ELENA: No, Salvatore. You'd better go. It's my father.

SALVATORE: Good, this way we can finally talk. I'll convince him this time.

ELENA: He won't be convinced, Salvatore. He has other plans for me.

SALVATORE: Who?

ELENA: The son of one of his colleagues. Don't act that way. We'll talk about it later. Wait for me Thursday at the Cinema Paradiso. I'll be coming with the five o'clock bus.
(SALVATORE *looks with longing as* ELENA *drives away with her father.* ELENA *gives him a meaningful look through the window.* SALVATORE *returns the look, but stands there motionless, with a grim expression, like someone who knows how to take the treacherous blows of life. The car drives off and with it* ELENA. *Their eyes hang on the same thread. The thread of hope and now of fear.*)

79: CINEMA PARADISO. ENTRANCE. EXT. MORNING
The poster of Il Grido *hangs on the billboard outside the theatre.* SPACCAFICO *replaces* 'THURSDAY' *with a* 'TODAY' *sticker. The* CHARWOMAN *is washing the floor of the lobby.* SPACCAFICO *shouts up to* SALVATORE, *who is in the projectionist's booth.* SPACCAFICIO *says that tomorrow he'll be leaving and today is his last day on the job, and he's sorry.*

SPACCAFICO: Totò, this is no film for the common herd. One day'll be more than enough . . . So tonight, please set up tomorrow's film, so the projectionist who is coming will find it ready.

SALVATORE: OK . . .
(SPACCAFICO *understands* SALVATORE's *sadness.*)

SPACCAFICO: Cheer up, Totò. I'll be here waiting for you. No one's taking your job away from you. Don't worry!

80: SQUARE AND PROJECTION BOOTH, CINEMA
PARADISO. EXT/INT. DAY
The bus has pulled into the square but among the people getting out

61

there is no sign of ELENA. SALVATORE *stands nervously up in the window of the projection booth, glances at his watch. It's already five-thirty and she hasn't come. He checks the projector. The first part has just begun and the reel is full of film.*

The first part is now about to finish, the reel is almost empty, and ELENA *still isn't there.* SALVATORE *is extremely nervous, worried, mortified by his meeting with her* FATHER. *He sees* ELENA's *face pulling away in the car. Thinks back over her terrible confession. He paces back and forth, as if he were in a prison cell, thinking up solutions . . . The stair light finally goes on: there she is!* SALVATORE *dashes over and down the stairs to meet her. He comes down the final turn of the spiral staircase and finds himself face to face with* ALFREDO, *who is slowly making his way up with the help of his cane.* SALVATORE *freezes to the spot.* ALFREDO *senses his disappointment.*
ALFREDO: You weren't expecting *me?*
SALVATORE: (*Nervously*) No, Alfredo, I was coming to help you . . .
ALFREDO: (*Smiling*) You were expecting her? Huh?
    (SALVATORE *doesn't answer. He's too worried, too upset.*
    ALFREDO *climbs another step, whispering.*)
    . . . It's a nasty business waiting by yourself. In company it's better. No? . . . Then I'll leave.
    (*As usual* ALFREDO's *sweetness comforts* SALVATORE, *indeed suddenly gives him a bold idea, one that quiets his nervousness. He puts a hand on* ALFREDO's *shoulder.*)
SALVATORE: Alfredo, I need your help!

81: ROAD TO THE CITY. EXT. AFTERNOON
The Balilla speeds as fast as it can down the road to the city, where ELENA's *family has gone to live.* SALVATORE *drives along in a state of agitation. The idea of having to leave without seeing* ELENA *is his obsession. An obsession he refuses to accept . . .*

82: CINEMA PARADISO. PROJECTION BOOTH. INT.
AFTERNOON
The second part has begun, the reel is full. For the first time in many years, ALFREDO *is alone in the booth, sitting in front of the projector, and he feels helpless. Not only because he's blind, but also because*

there is nothing he can do for SALVATORE. *A strange agitation comes over him, as if he were experiencing the same anxiety troubling his 'Totò' at that moment. Meanwhile, the film rolls on and with it, time, minutes . . .*

83: CITY. EXT. AFTERNOON
SALVATORE *has already reached the city. He slows down at the bus terminus. Looks at the people waiting, but she is not there . . .*
He asks several girls in front of the University. But they haven't seen her . . .
He phones from a phone booth. But nobody answers. His self-control is about to give way to desperation . . .

84: CINEMA PARADISO. PROJECTION BOOTH. INT.
AFTERNOON
On the reel there is less film. Like an hourglass with the sand trickling through . . .

85: ELENA'S HOUSE IN THE CITY. EXT/INT. AFTERNOON
SALVATORE *comes streaking up in front of her house. He screeches to a stop, dashes out like greased lightning. His nerves are tense, a slight tremor runs through his whole body. He rings the bell, but nobody answers. A* MAN *who lives in the building opens the front door and comes out.* SALVATORE *seizes the chance and climbs up to the third floor. He pounds on the door furiously, almost cracking his knuckles. But all to no avail; there is nobody at home. He shrieks, panic-stricken.*
SALVATORE: Open up! Open up! Elenaaa!
    (*And in fact, there is somebody inside:* ELENA'S MOTHER. *She sits there immobile, without a word. The pounding on the door reverberates in the room, but she does not budge, determined to ignore that desperate message.*)

86: CINEMA PARADISO. PROJECTION BOOTH. INT.
AFTERNOON
The reel spins faster. The film is almost ended. By now there is very little time . . .

87: ROAD TO THE VILLAGE. EXT. SUNDOWN
And SALVATORE *is on his way home, defeated. He drives as fast as
he can. He is in a terrible state, can't figure out what's happened.
Can't explain it. And that's what hurts.*

88: CINEMA PARADISO. PROJECTION BOOTH. INT. SUNDOWN
*The words 'THE END' appear on the screen . . . and the film runs
out, leaving the projector turning uselessly. ALFREDO is alarmed. He
can hear that the film is finished, but doesn't know where to begin.
He gropes around. He's scared. Like a little boy calls his mother
when he's lost in a crowd, so old ALFREDO calls SALVATORE.*
ALFREDO: Totooooò! Totooooò!
> (*The few people down in the audience start whistling and
> complaining about the film they haven't understood.*)
SPECTATORS: Lights! Christ, what a piece of crap!! We want our
money back!!! Heeeeey!! Bandits!!
> (*Others are shouting that they like the film.*)

89: CINEMA PARADISO. ENTRANCE. EXT. SUNDOWN
The Balilla screeches to a stop in front of the theatre. SALVATORE
darts out and runs to the stairs . . .

90: CINEMA PARADISO. PROJECTION BOOTH. INT. SUNDOWN
SALVATORE *turns the lights on in the theatre and turns off the
projector, trying to calm down* ALFREDO, *who has got to his feet,
frightened.*
ALFREDO: But where'd you go, Totò?!!
SALVATORE: I'm here! Take it easy! Take it easy!
> (*And he folds him into his arms, like calming down a little boy
> who has had a nightmare. He whispers, still out of breath:*)
> Sit down, sit down . . .
> (ALFREDO *quiets down as* SALVATORE *lowers him into a chair,
> and asks him the only question upon which his last hope
> depends.*)
> Did she come?
ALFREDO: No, nobody came.
> (*And he embraces him, almost as if to comfort him in his great
> disappointment. For* SALVATORE *it's really the end: she's not*

*coming. Tomorrow he'll be leaving without having seen her
again.*
SALVATORE's *hands remove the photographs of Amedeo Nazzari
and of* ELENA *from the wall, slip them into one of his pockets.
Now the hands open the metal containers of tomorrow's film, take
out the reels to set them up, pick up the receipt – his last before
leaving – and with the same mechanical gesture, hang it on a
nail, as usual.*)

91: ROME. VARIOUS SETTINGS, MILITARY LIFE. EXT/
INT. DAY/NIGHT
A wild frenetic sequence, set to the pace of military life . . .
SALVATORE, *in uniform with close-cropped hair, answers his
superior, shouts:*
SALVATORE: Radio Operator Di Vita Salvatore! Third Battalion,
    Ninth Company, sir!!!

Target practice. SALVATORE *fires all the shots in the cartridge, one
after the other . . .*

A SECOND LIEUTENANT *barks out a march rhythm in the blazing
sun.*
SECOND LIEUTENANT: One, two, one, two!! Attention! Left
    march!
    (SALVATORE *sneaks out of line, goes over and slips a letter into
    the mailbox and hurries back to his place.*)

On one of the public phones in a square of Rome, SALVATORE *is
phoning* ELENA. *Nobody answers. He slams down the receiver, as the
line of* SOLDIERS *waits its turn . . .*

Night-time. A large plastic bag full of water. A thud. SALVATORE
*wakes up with a start in a lake of ice water. He lets out a terrified
shriek as the others laugh, protected by the dark.*
SALVATORE: Aaaaaaah! Heeeeeelp!!

In the large dormitory, the SERGEANT *is handing out the mail. He
throws a pile of letters on* SALVATORE's *bunk. They are his letters to*
ELENA, *stamped* 'ADDRESS UNKNOWN'.

65

Mess duty. SALVATORE *is washing up, in a sea of water and grease.*
He rinses a pan full of tomato sauce with a tap hose. A spurt of red
water splatters him in the face.

A training run. Another letter which SALVATORE *drops into the*
mailbox . . .

A cold, rainy night. SALVATORE *stands stiff as a poker in front of*
the ammunition depot. It is his first guard duty. Soaked to the skin,
gazing wide-eyed into empty space.

COLONEL's *office.*
SALVATORE: (*Aggressively*) Colonel, I was supposed to spend ten
    days here and it's been about a year, and I haven't ever
    gone home. I'd like a furlough, at least!

SALVATORE *is in the guardhouse. A cold, dark, filthy cell. His*
nerves start to give way. He bows his head in despair.

Hospital. SALVATORE *is exhausted, run-down. The night-stand is*
jammed with medicines. He lies in bed without moving, staring off
into empty space, and repeats obsessively in a low voice, as if talking
to himself.
SALVATORE: Elena . . .Elena . . . Elena . . .
    (*He has touched the extreme of suffering, a young man who has*
    been denied love and affection, his rights, freedom. A NURSE
    comes up.)
NURSE: Di Vita Salvatore, get ready, your discharge has come
    through.
    (SALVATORE *registers this information with his eyes and nods*
    absently.)

92: GIANCALDO. SQUARE AND STREETS. EXT. DAY
The bus disappears around the corner leaving SALVATORE *standing*
there alone. It is a blazing hot day. The sirocco wind blows the
yellow dust in all directions. The square is empty, the billboard in
front of the closed movie house announces a Western. SALVATORE
puts his suitcase on the ground, looks around. Everything exactly the
same, immobile. Only one new feature: in the café there's a jukebox

playing 'Estate' sung by Milva.
SALVATORE *turns towards the Cinema Paradiso. The projectionist is at the window of the booth, smoking a cigarette. Who knows who he is, where he came from. A hot flurry of dust.* SALVATORE *turns and sees a dog leaping around him, wagging its tail. It's the dog that kept him company during his nights beneath the window.* SALVATORE *gives a start of joy, drops his suitcase and leans over to stroke him. Then he hugs him, as if he were an old friend.*

93: ALFREDO'S HOUSE. INT. AFTERNOON
SALVATORE *goes to see* ALFREDO. *He is still in bed, has just woken up. He is glad to hear his 'Totò'. He feels his forehead, his eyes and cheeks, as if to 'see' him.*

ALFREDO: You're thinner . . . You can tell you've not been treated well.
   (*As usual, you can't hide anything from* ALFREDO. SALVATORE *senses something different in him that he can't figure out, like some wild restlessness within*).

SALVATORE: They tell me you never go out, never talk to anybody. Why?

ALFREDO: Totò, sooner or later there comes a time when talking or keeping quiet is the same thing. So it's better to shut up. (*Changing his tone*) It's hot in here. Totò, take me to the beach.

94: BEACH AND WATERFRONT. EXT. AFTERNOON
The sea is ruffled and the air is less sultry, easier to breathe.
SALVATORE *and* ALFREDO *walk slowly along the waterfront.*
ALFREDO *totters slightly, holds on to* SALVATORE, *who is telling him something very funny.*

SALVATORE: At the Christmas party the lieutenant pinches a girl's ass. The girl turns around: it's the daughter of the commanding officer. The lieutenant is scared to death and says: 'Miss, if your heart is as hard as what I have just touched, I'm done for!'
   (*And they roar with laughter. They look like two old school buddies telling each other dirty jokes. They stop beside a low wall.* ALFREDO *knows that those laughs are simply a way of uselessly dancing around the countless things that are troubling*

SALVATORE. *And he breaks the ice, while* SALVATORE *is still laughing.*)

ALFREDO: (*Seriously*) Did you ever see her again?
(SALVATORE'*s laughter dies away, taken off-guard as he is. Then he lights a cigarette.*)

SALVATORE: No. And nobody knows where she is.

ALFREDO: It was probably meant to be like this. Each of us has a star to follow. So now what are you thinking of doing?
(*It's a terrible question, and* SALVATORE *has no answer to it. In fact, would rather not even talk about it. He changes his tone, as if he hadn't heard it, laughs, trying again to cling to the funny jokes he heard during military service.*)

SALVATORE: Listen to this one . . . The commander says to the sergeant: 'You remember that windmill that used to be there?' 'Yes, sir, I remember: the mill's gone but the wind's still there!'
(*And he bursts into nervous laughter. But this time* ALFREDO *remains cold, unmoved, does not laugh with him.* SALVATORE *gradually falls silent. He doesn't know what to say. For the first time in his life, he doesn't know what goal to aim for, doesn't know what to do. The cloud of smoke wreaths his nervous face, now he seems to relax, whispers:*)
You remember the story of the soldier and the princess?
(ALFREDO *nods his head.*)

SALVATORE: Now I understand why the soldier went away just before the end. That's right, just one more night and the princess would have been his. But she, also, could not have kept her promise. And . . . that would have been terrible, he would have died from it. So instead, for ninety-nine nights at least he had lived with the illusion that she was there waiting for him . . .
(*This time* SALVATORE *is the one to explain something to* ALFREDO. *And* ALFREDO *realizes how bitter his story is and, above all, that the boy standing there is no longer a boy . . .*)

ALFREDO: Do like the soldier, Totò! Go away! This land is cursed.
(*They are now leaning against a boat on the beach.* ALFREDO *goes on whispering his words.*)
When you're here every day you feel like you're at the centre

of the universe, it seems like nothing ever changes. Then you
go away, one year, two . . . And when you come back,
everything's different. The thread has broken. You don't
find those you were looking for, your things no longer exist.
Isn't that the case? . . . You've got to go away a long time, for
many, many years, before coming back and finding your
people again, the land where you were born . . . But not now,
it's impossible. Now you're blinder than I am.
(*Intense words, straight from the heart, and* SALVATORE *is
spellbound. He whispers with a smile:*)

SALVATORE: Who said that? Gary Cooper, James Stewart, Henry
Fonda? Huh?
(ALFREDO *also gives a gentle smile*)

ALFREDO: No, Totò, nobody said it. *I* say it! Life's not like you
saw it in the movies. Life . . . is harder.
(*He lays his hand on* SALVATORE's *shoulder, gives it a hard
squeeze.*)
Get out! Go back to Rome. You're young, the world is yours!
And I'm old . . . I don't want to hear *you* talk any more, I
want to hear talk *about* you.
(SALVATORE *gives a shudder that runs through his very soul. The
setting sun lies colourless on the horizon.*)

95: VARIOUS SETTINGS. EXT/INT. NIGHT
Night. The square is empty. SALVATORE *is sitting on the church steps.
His head in his hands. He has to make a decision: leave or stay. And
why? . . .*
'*What decision will he make?*' *is the question that keeps* ALFREDO
awake, in his hot dark bedroom . . .
MARIA, *his mother, also can't get to sleep. She knows, senses, that her
son is on the verge of an important turning-point. But what will he
decide? What will happen? . . .*
Also LIA, *his sister, feels a strange, heavy tension in the air. And
doesn't sleep. She's probably wondering where* SALVATORE *is at that
hour . . .*
*He's sitting on the ground. But even if he were to go to bed he wouldn't
sleep. He rubs his face with his hand. The church bell chimes four
a.m. . . .*

ALMOST THIRTY YEARS LATER, *another distant bell is chiming four a.m. And* SALVATORE *is once again wide awake. He is thinking, with his hand on his face, just like then. And the same decision to make: what to do? Stretched out beside a sleeping* WOMAN, *he goes on staring at the window. Outside, the storm has passed. The long memory has almost faded, only the sound of a train surfaces in his mind* . . .

96: GIANCALDO RAILWAY STATION. EXT. DAY
It's the train that THIRTY YEARS EARLIER *had pulled into the station of his home town before leaving for Rome.* SALVATORE *hugs his* MOTHER *and* SISTER. *The moment has come to say goodbye to* ALFREDO. *The old man is deeply moved. A heart-rending trembling comes into his husky voice.*

ALFREDO: Don't come back any more, don't think about us, don't turn round, don't write, don't give in to nostalgia. Forget us all. If you can't bear it and come back, don't come looking for me, I won't let you into the house, you understand?
(They clasp each other tightly, as if they knew they wouldn't be meeting again . . .)
SALVATORE: Thanks for all you've done for me.
ALFREDO: Whatever you do, love it like you loved that projection booth of the Paradiso when you were little . . .
(The train moves now. Hands wave in the air, drawing further and further away. The PRIEST *has arrived at the last moment and waves goodbye from the distance.)*
PRIEST: *(Shouting)* Goodbye, Totooooooò!!! I got here too late. What a shame!
(The figure of ALFREDO *and the others can no longer be distinguished. Only a distant blur at the end of the track.)*

97: PUNTA RAISI AIRPORT. EXT. DAY
THIRTY YEARS LATER, *a plane flies over Sicily. It lands on the runway that seems to emerge from the sea and flatten out towards the slopes of the dark mountains.* SALVATORE'S *face appears among the clouds reflected in one of the plane windows. He has the tense look of the man who suddenly comes home after the adventure of life has carried him afar, wandering the world, where he has forgotten everything. From the plane window to another window* . . .

98: SUPERHIGHWAY. INT/EXT. DAY

. . . the window of the taxi-cab driving SALVATORE *to his home town.
The scenery moving by on either side of the road summons up sweet
memories. A lot of things have changed, but the colours are still the
same. The yellow running through the entire landscape is
unmistakable. And all those black birds perched in a row on the
guard-rail are crows.
The cab now approaches the outskirts of Giancaldo. But if the sign
hadn't been there with the name on it, it could be an entirely different
place . . .*

99: SALVATORE'S MOTHER'S HOUSE. EXT/INT. DAY

The house where SALVATORE'S MOTHER *lives is also new, nearer the
sea.
The old lady is sitting alone in an armchair in the parlour, knitting a
white sweater. Her hands move very swiftly, almost mechanically.
The hands of a woman who is waiting. The front doorbell rings twice.*
MARIA *stops short. That is what she has been waiting for. She
mumbles in excitement.*

MARIA: It's Totò . . . I knew it . . .

> (*And she scrambles to her feet, dropping her knitting in the chair,
> one needle dangling over the edge. She hurries off, forgetting that
> she still has the ball of white yarn in her apron pocket. And the
> yarn runs off the needles and the knitting comes undone quickly as
> she moves about the house, goes down the stairs to the front door.
> There the yarn stops and* MARIA's *excited voice is heard.*)

MARIA'S VOICE: (*Off-screen*) Totò! . . .

SALVATORE'S VOICE: (*Off-screen*) How are you, Mamma? . . .

> (*The camera now moves, discovering them through the parlour
> window, hugging each other outside the front door. Under the
> curious eyes of an old bored dog.*)

100: SALVATORE'S MOTHER'S HOUSE. INT. DAY

MARIA *is no longer wearing an apron. Mother and son are sitting side
by side at the kitchen table . . .*

MARIA: Lia'll be so glad to see you, you'll see. And you won't
recognize the kids any more, they're grown up by now.

SALVATORE: (*Smiling*) They're always writing to me saying they
want to come to Rome!

71

(SALVATORE *looks around; it's a place he's never seen before, and yet it's his mother's house!*)

MARIA: See how pretty the house is? We did everything over. (*Smiling*) If it hadn't been for you! (*Getting up*) Come, I've a surprise . . .
(*She takes him by the hand and leads him out to the hallway. SALVATORE looks at her and feels a pang. She seems smaller, age withers the body, she is slightly stooped, her hair is gathered into a knot at the back of her head.*)
You must be tired. If you want to rest, there's time before the funeral.

SALVATORE: (*Interrupting her*) No, Mamma, it only takes an hour by air, you know.

MARIA: (*Smiling, ironically*) You shouldn't tell me that now. After all these years!
(SALVATORE *gets the message, feels guilty. Thinking about it, it seems incredible that he has never come before.* MARIA *opens a door, steps aside to let her son in, whispers:*)
I put all your things in here. Go in, go in . . .
(SALVATORE *takes a few steps, is flabbergasted at the sight of his old room perfectly reconstructed and preserved. It looks like a museum, the museum of the past. Despite the bed, the clothes in the cupboard, the books on the shelves, it is perfectly clear that no one has ever lived in it and never will live in it.* MARIA *senses his perturbation, remains standing in the doorway as if to leave him alone . . .*
SALVATORE *goes over to the bed, looks around: the old 8mm movie camera, the projector, his documentaries, the bicycle hanging on the wall, the photographs of his favourite movie stars. But what mostly catches his eye is a tiny framed photograph:* SALVATORE *as a little boy and* ALFREDO, *standing smiling in front of the Cinema Paradiso. Strange, at that time* ALFREDO *was younger than he is now! It's as if he were standing there before him one last time. That impressive figure, his good-natured but firm look, touches his heart.*
From ALFREDO's *smiling face to . . .*)

101: GIANCALDO. MAIN STREET AND SQUARE. EXT. DAY
. . . the coffin where his old blind friend rests for ever. The funeral

72

procession winds its way down the main street. At the intersections,
cars stop to let the black hearse pass by. People cross themselves. The
old men remove their hats. Store shutters are lowered. Then, when the
procession has passed by, the cars start up again, the old men put their
hats back on, the shutters are pulled up.
SALVATORE *is in the front row with his* MOTHER, *next to* ALFREDO's
WIDOW. SIGNORA ANNA *says in a whisper, her eyes fixed on the*
coffin:
ANNA: He would have been happy you came, Totò. He always
 talked about you. Always! Right to the end! He was terribly
 fond of you . . .
 (*Tears come to her, she is unable to say any more.* SALVATORE
 gives her a hug, deeply touched by her words.)
He left two things for you. Come see me before you leave.
(SALVATORE *nods his head. He gazes intensely at the coffin*
covered with flowers and is grieved as if he were ashamed never to
have come to see the man who had been like a father to him. But
why had he forgotten him? Up in front, leading the procession, he
sees a young priest with an altar boy beside him, and these figures
are also like chisels scraping the rust off his soul and bringing old
feelings to light again.
The procession reaches the square. The dark column stands etched
in the dazzling early-afternoon light. SIGNORA ANNA *motions*
the driver and the procession comes to a halt. It is ALFREDO's *last*
farewell to the place where he had spent the best years of his life:
the Cinema Paradiso. Everyone turns to look and SALVATORE
also turns, taken by surprise . . . It has fallen to pieces: doors and
windows boarded shut, crumbling walls, a piece of the sign
dangling down, weeds and mildew in the cracks and on the roof.
The square has changed completely, is unrecognizable.
Buildings, stores, signboards and lines of cars creeping at a
snail's pace in a deafening chorus of honking horns. And the
central square has turned into a parking lot jammed with cars and
motorcycles. SALVATORE *turns slowly to look behind him,*
towards the small crowd, and is entranced by the unexpected sight
of faces that he recognizes at once, despite the many years that
have gone by: the MAN AT THE BOX OFFICE, *the* USHER *who*
also served as bill-poster, the CHARWOMAN, *the*
CARABINIERE SERGEANT, *and further on behind* ROSA *and*

ANGELO, *the lovebirds who had met in the movie house and then got married. They all have white hair. And they too have recognized him, give little hello nods and gestures. Another face he seems to recognize: why sure, it's* SPACCAFICO, *the owner. How old he's become! He also looks up and his eyes meet* SALVATORE's. *A hello nod.* SALVATORE *makes his way over to him through the crowd. They shake hands heartily, without a word, both touched. The procession starts up again.*)

SALVATORE: (*Under his breath*) How long's it been shut?

SPACCAFICO: Six years ago this May. No one came any more. You know better than me, Mr Di Vita, the crisis, television, videos. By now the movie business is only a dream. The city's bought it now to make a new parking lot. Next Saturday they're tearing it down . . . A pity! . . .
(SALVATORE *is disconcerted, irritated by that 'Mr Di Vita'. Besides, finding out that the movie house is to be torn down depresses him; after all, it's a piece of his life . . . And all those curious faces staring at him.*)

SALVATORE: But why do you call me 'Mr Di Vita'? It didn't used to be that way . . .

SPACCAFICO: Well, it's hard to call an important person by his first name. But if it really matters to you, I'll call you . . . (*Smiling*) Totò! . . .
(SALVATORE *smiles at that. Meanwhile, the procession has reached the church.* SALVATORE *excuses himself and goes over to the hearse. Old* SPACCAFICO *watches him go, then says, almost to himself:*)

SPACCAFICO: Bless you, Totò.
(*The coffin is unloaded.* SALVATORE *has asked to be one of the bearers into the church. As he moves off slowly with that weight on his shoulder, somebody catches his eye on the other side of the sidewalk. An old woman, sixty or seventy years old, with a plastic bag in her hand. She crosses herself quickly.* SALVATORE *recognizes her: she was the one he made love with for the first time.* TERESA, *the prostitute. The coffin is carried into the church, followed by the little procession.*

102: SALVATORE'S MOTHER'S HOUSE. EXT/INT. EVENING
The little house is sunk in the darkness of evening and the ground floor

74

windows are lit up. The rustling of the sea can be heard.
The family is having supper. The table is set with the finest silver and
the company china has been brought out. LIA *is also there with her*
husband, ALFIO, *and their two children.* FILIPPO, *fifteen, and* SARA,
thirteen. The television is on, but the sound has been turned practically
all the way down. SALVATORE's *presence arouses a special*
excitement. The children look at their uncle with a certain awe, after
all they don't really know him.

SARA: (*Playfully*) Uncle, the next time Granny comes to Rome, I
    want to come along too. I want to see what you do when you
    work . . .

SALVATORE: (*Smiling*) Fine. But I warn you, there isn't much to
    see. I sell much more smoke than fire . . .
    (*The* CHILDREN *laugh. At the sight of them,* LIA, ALFIO *and*
    MARIA *also smile.*)

ALFIO (*To* SALVATORE) Watch out, don't get too familiar with
    those two (*indicating the children*), they're worse than
    cannibals. They'll take advantage.
    (*Everybody laughs again. Even* MARIA *laughs a lot.*
    SALVATORE *looks at her: he had never seen her laugh like that,*
    amused, at peace.)

FILIPPO: You leaving tomorrow, Uncle?
    (SALVATORE *doesn't know what to say. He feels drunk. It has*
    been a day of violent upheavals, a series of almost overwhelming
    emotions and now he knows nothing: on the one hand, he'd like to
    stay, let himself drift on the sweet tide of family life, be
    completely carried off by the rolling waves of his own past; on the
    other, he wishes he had never come. He forces himself to smile
    again.)

SALVATORE: I don't know, Filippo. I don't know . . .
    (*They go on eating, but* SALVATORE *isn't very hungry. He peers*
    at LIA *eating out of the corner of his eye, feels deeply bound to*
    her: she has a few white hairs and light wrinkles line her face.
    Then he looks at her husband, ALFIO; *he's going bald but he tries*
    to hide it by combing over the little hair left. Who knows what
    their marriage is like, he wonders. He looks back at LIA, *and it's*
    as if she sensed it: she looks up, guesses the nature of his thoughts,
    imagines what he is trying to figure out, a blush colours her cheeks
    and she smiles. SALVATORE *returns a conniving smile.*

The ringing of a phone. SARA *starts to get up to go and answer it,
but* MARIA *stops her with a glance of the eye.*)
MARIA: (*To* SALVATORE) It must be for you . . . They've been
calling all afternoon. They wanted to know if you're leaving
this evening or tomorrow . . .
(*Everyone turns to* SALVATORE *with questioning looks, making
him feel even more restless and undecided. The phone goes on
ringing.*)

103: CINEMA PARADISO. EXT. DAY
The TRAFFIC COPS *are trying to break the front door down with their
shoulders. Once, twice, and at last, the door flies open with a screech,
kicking up a cloud of dust.* SALVATORE *enters by himself . . .*

104: CINEMA PARADISO. PROJECTION BOOTH. INT. DAY
SALVATORE'*s silhouette stands out against the light in the open door.
Slowly he makes his way into the empty theatre. A thick layer of dust
lends everything a grey, rarefied look. The light streaming in from the
windows up above teems with strange motes of dust, like a haze.
Cobwebs hang like long veils from the ceiling.* SALVATORE *walks
down the middle aisle. The rows of seats are unhinged, what was once
the wooden veneer has warped from the dampness. He looks around as
if he were thumbing through the album of his memories.
The screen dangles from its frame. The emergency exits are boarded
and nailed shut. Observing the emptiness of the theatre,* SALVATORE
*has the feeling he can hear the howling, the whistling and voices of the
audience, as he remembers it. But only for one brief moment, then the
silence returns.
A mouse creeps along one wall, stops near a pile of dust.* SALVATORE
*is attracted by that little grey mass. He goes over as the mouse scampers
off, takes a closer look and recognizes the shape of half a lion's head
covered with dust. He moves it with his foot, then looks up at the
projection booth, repeating the same gesture of bygone years. But the
lion's head is no longer there, only the outline of it on the wall, and
cobwebs have covered the holes of the booth, those little square
openings that had caused him such long suffering as a little boy . . .*
SALVATORE *now climbs up the spiral staircase. Each step kicks up a
little cloud of dust.
The little booth, yellow with fumes, appears before him again. Now it*

*looks like some big, empty cave. The projector is no longer there, nor
the equipment. Who knows where they junked them?! The only thing
left is a clump of film strips still attached to the wall: trailers, Part One
endings, etc . . . There he had kissed* ELENA *for the first time, and
strips of film like those had grazed their faces. Now they are caught up
in the coils of cobwebs. And where the film-winder once stood, the
nails remain with thousands of yellowing receipts. Of all the films
shown at the Cinema Paradiso Palace. And three more boxfuls of
them are on the floor.*
*And the windows overlooking the square are bolted shut and the glass
broken.* SALVATORE *peers out of one of the cracks in the window and
sees the village . . . which is now a city. A different world he no longer
knows.*

105: CAFÉ IN SQUARE. INT/EXT. DAY
The café in the square has been completely renovated. The CASHIER
and BARMEN *have young, unfamiliar faces.* SALVATORE *holds out
the receipt with a tip.*
SALVATORE: A double whisky, please.
> (*Several* BOYS *are sitting at the corner tables, talking about girls.
> Others stand playing 'war games', shake around to the obsessive
> strains of some electronic tune. A man comes up to* SALVATORE
> *and asks for his autograph. Then* SALVATORE *turns to the
> plate-glass window overlooking the main street, where the
> workers' club once was. And like a flash, a shudder freezes him to
> the spot . . .*
> *Two steps away from him, through the glass, a stunning vision,
> which casts him beyond time, chills his blood: there before him is*
> ELENA! *But she is still young, young as she was then! Sweet,
> luminous, alluring, exactly the way he saw her the first time at the
> station. She is waiting to go across the street with a bunch of
> books under her arm . . . Have the passing years had no effect on
> her? Or is she an hallucination? No! It's a dream! Or is he dead
> too, like* ALFREDO? SALVATORE *doesn't know how to explain it.
> And he is suddenly seized by a feeling of panic. His glass drops to
> the floor . . . As the* GIRL *walks off . . .*)

106: GIANCALDO. STREET. EXT. DAY
At the age of fifty-five, SALVATORE *feels no scruples about wandering*

the streets of his home town, spying from a distance on an eighteen-year-old girl. There's nothing he can do about it. He stares at her with the amazement of someone who discovers that miracles exist. Now he is nearer to her. How lovely she is! It's her, no doubt about it! Exactly the same. Except she has a different hair-do and is wearing different clothes: ELENA *didn't wear slacks. The* GIRL *goes up to a parked motorcycle. She removes the padlock and fastens her books to the rack.* SALVATORE *is standing there a few steps away, and without stopping to think, moves a little closer, discreetly, politely.*

SALVATORE: Excuse me, Miss . . .
> (*She turns to look at him, indifferent, but friendly. He looks at her wonderful blue eyes.*)

I'm so sorry, I thought you were someone else.

GIRL: (*Shrugging*) Well.
> (*She has already started the motor of her bike. A flip of the accelerator and off she goes, her hair flying in the wind.* SALVATORE *follows her with his eyes until she disappears around the corner.*)

107: SALVATORE'S MOTHER'S HOUSE. INT. AFTERNOON
The old shots of ELENA *getting off the train and walking away, casting a curious look at the camera . . .*
SALVATORE *is watching her again, projected on the white wall of his room. He also watches the other shots of those happy long-gone days: the picnic; she at the beach, smiling, joyful . . . And again* SALVATORE *doesn't understand, or doesn't want to understand. But these scenes could have been shot yesterday, so identical to* ELENA *is the girl he saw on the street . . . And the wound which he thought had healed years ago, starts bleeding again. The lingering note of suffering for a romance that had ended without his ever knowing why, and the endless explanations that had been sifted through by his young mind, start slipping through his soul again, like those shots slipping again through an old 8mm projector.*
Through the crack of the door, MARIA *sees those images on the wall,* SALVATORE *rocking his head back and forth slowly, like he used to do as a boy when he cried. She somehow feels his grief, his bitterness, lowers her eyes and walks away without a word, as the little shiny rectangle on the wall remains blank, empty . . . And* SALVATORE *sits*

*there gazing at it, as if he saw other scenes which his camera never
set down on film, only his memory.*

108: HIGH SCHOOL. STREETS AND LITTLE SQUARE. EXT.
DAY
The HIGH SCHOOL STUDENTS *are coming out after school. Happy,
young faces. That* GIRL'*s motorcycle can be seen in a rear-view
mirror.* SALVATORE *is at the wheel of the car* ALFIO *has lent him.
He has obviously followed that motorcycle before. He waits with an
eagerness he thought he had long lost, a determination to understand,
to get to the bottom of the matter, which frightens him and at the
same time overwhelms him hopelessly.
And here she comes. She unlocks the padlock and prepares to speed
off.* SALVATORE *starts the motor and follows her a short distance
away. The* GIRL *heads for the new residential district on the
outskirts.*

109: SALVATORE'S MOTHER'S HOUSE. INT. DAY
MARIA *is setting the table.* LIA *and her family are eating at her
house today.* SALVATORE *is sitting again, with a lighted cigarette,
gazing through the window at the shrubs tossing in the wind and the
rolling sea. The air whistling through the cracks of the windows lends
a heaviness to the silence, like the troubled look on his face.* MARIA
glances at him.
MARIA: What are you thinking, Totò?
    (SALVATORE *looks at the old woman's lovely face, a faint smile
    on his lips. There was always something like an unspoken rule
    between them, the rule of silence, of unconfessed complicity.
    And now he feels that rule has to be broken. He speaks quietly,
    as if to curb the tumult of his feelings of guilt.*)
SALVATORE: I was thinking . . . that we've never talked,
    Mamma . . . When I was little I saw you as if you were
    already old. That's probably true with all kids . . . Who
    knows?
    (*She nods, then sits down before him. He strokes her old,
    skinny, heavily veined hands . . .*)
    But only now do I realize you were young, you were
    beautiful, had a whole life before you. But how . . .
    (*Sighing*) how could you have lived alone all that time, with

79

no one to look after you? You could have remarried . . . Why not? At the time I probably wouldn't have understood, but I would have later . . .

(MARIA *doesn't answer, but she is not troubled. An inner peace lends her a sweet, quiet expression. Then she too agrees to break the rule of silence.*)

MARIA: I never had anybody. If that's what you think . . . I didn't want anybody. I always remained faithful. First to your father, then to you, to Lia. (*With a shrug*) That's the way I'm made, there's nothing I can do about it. (*Smiling*) And you're like me, you're too honest and too attached to the things you love . . . But I don't know if that's a good thing. Faithfulness is a bad business. If you're faithful, you're always alone!

(SALVATORE *is immersed in the profound truth of those words. And he says nothing. The silence is broken by the ringing of the phone. A menacing sound, which* SALVATORE *cannot bear. He knows they are calling him from Rome, gives a nervous gesture, stands up and pulls out the plug. The silence returns, the whistling of the wind.* MARIA *lowers her eyes.*)

It's my fault! It would have been better if I hadn't called you . . .

(SALVATORE *sits down again, leaning closer to her. He stubs out his cigarette in the already overflowing ashtray.*)

SALVATORE: (*Whispering*) No . . . It's nothing to do with you. It's just that I was scared of coming back. Now, after all these years, I thought I was strong, that I had forgotten lots of things. Instead, I find it's quite the opposite, as if I had never left. And yet, I look at Lia and feel as if I didn't know her, and you, Mamma . . . I abandoned you, ran away like a thief, thought only of myself, and never gave you an explanation . . .

MARIA: (*Interrupting him*) And I never asked for one! You have nothing to explain. I always thought that what you did was right, and that was that. With no beating around the bush . . . (*Smiling, playing it down*) Only one thing made me suffer: bolting the door shut before going to bed at night . . .

SALVATORE: You never used to do that!

(*She smiles like a little girl who is about to confess the fibs she has told.*)

MARIA: No, no . . . When you used to work at the movies, I could never get to sleep at night until you came home. Then when you arrived, I pretended to be asleep, but I heard all your movements. Then when you fell asleep, I'd get up and bolt the door. Then, when you left, every time I did it, I felt as if I had left somebody outside the door, far away . . .
(SALVATORE *listens to his* MOTHER's *words, surprised and entranced by the poetry of her way of speaking . . .*)
But you were right to leave. You succeeded in doing what you wanted to do . . . (*Sighing*) When I call you, a different woman always answers. I pretend I know them so they won't have to go through the embarrassment of introducing themselves. (*Smiling*) I'm sure they take me for a crazy old woman. But so far I've never heard one voice that really loves you . . . I would have known. And yet, I'd like to see you . . . settled down . . . fall in love . . . (*Gazing into his eyes*) But your life's there. Here there are nothing but ghosts, Totò! Let it go.
(*She has said this with a subtle allusiveness in her voice. And* SALVATORE *realizes she has always known everything. But he doesn't answer her. They look at each other a long time without speaking. Their rule of conniving silence has come back into play, as before, forever. It is her expression that tells him to leave, to take the plane and fly away . . .*)

110: SMALL SQUARE AND HOUSE. INT/EXT. EVENING
But SALVATORE *has not taken his* MOTHER's *advice. He has not left. Something holds him there still, leads him to go on looking.*
The GIRL's *motorcycle is parked in the courtyard beyond the gate of a small house. He is studying it from inside the car parked in a corner of the small square, near a café. He has been there some while, but is not nervous, waits there with determination . . .*
Several windows in the house are lit, but no one can be seen through the curtains. Nothing but shadows pass by every now and then. Now the light in one of the windows goes out, and the light on the stair goes on. The front door opens and the GIRL *comes out with a tall, sturdy-looking, elegantly dressed* GENTLEMAN *around fifty. They converse but are too far away for their voices to be heard.* SALVATORE *watches them come out the gate and climb into a car. They look like father and*

81

daughter. The car now drives off and passes right by him. A gleam of light, the reflection from the headlights, falls on the GENTLEMAN'S *face. He recognizes him at once, from the birthmark on his temple . . .*
SALVATORE: (*To himself*) Boccia!
> (*His eyes flash, he's afraid he's understood. And now the craze to get to the bottom of it all gnaws away at him. There is no turning back.*)

III: CAFÉ AND SMALL SQUARE. INT/EXT. EVENING
SALVATORE'S *hands riffle through a phone directory. He is in the café, on the other side of the glass door leading to the little square. His finger runs down the column of names . . .*
SALVATORE: (*Mumbling*) His last name was Lo Meo, Vincenzo.
> (*He has already put the token into the slot and dials the number, looking at the two lit upstairs windows of that house, where the mystery of his life may be hiding.* SALVATORE *hears the first ring, his heart in his throat . . . A shadow appears in one of the windows. And a voice answers.*
VOICE ON TELEPHONE: Hello?
> (*It's a woman's voice.* SALVATORE *shuts his eyes, is about to speak, but the lump in his throat silences him . . .*)
VOICE ON TELEPHONE: Hello? Hello?
> (*He still hesitates, can't get a word out, as if he had lost his voice or didn't know what to say. He hangs up. The shadow at the window also hangs up, then disappears.*
> SALVATORE *is at a loss, sits down at one of the tables near the phone in the almost empty café. At the far end, a group of five people watching television.*)
BARMAN: You want something?
> (*And he turns back to the television.* SALVATORE *lights a cigarette. He is uncertain. Once again he has to take an important decision: redial the number and seek a face behind that shadow? Or forget the whole thing, the* GIRL, BOCCIA, *the shadow, and go away?*
> *Yes, best go away. He gets up and leaves. He can be seen through the window turning the corner. A pack of cigarettes and a lighter lie on the table, he has forgotten them. And the lighted cigarette burns down in the ashtray. A few moments have gone by.*
> *Footsteps, and a hand picks up the lighter and the cigarettes. It is*

SALVATORE *who now, on a sudden urge, slips another token into the slot.*
The shadow reappears at the window. The same voice as before.)

VOICE ON TELEPHONE: Hello, who's speaking?

(SALVATORE *answers at last, keeping his eyes shut, whispering:)*

SALVATORE: I'd like to speak to Signora Elena . . .

VOICE ON TELEPHONE: Speaking. Who is it, please?

(SALVATORE *feels a terrible pang, continues:)*

SALVATORE: Salvatore.

(*Silence, charged with tension. Then the voice continues weakly, as if puzzled.)*

VOICE ON TELEPHONE: Salvatore . . . who?

(*He runs his hand over his forehead, his eyes, as if to soothe the turmoil he feels inside.)*

SALVATORE: Di Vita. Salvatore Di Vita. Do you remember?

(*Another pause chilly, heavy.* SALVATORE *opens his eyes, looks at the window. Her shadow is motionless, as if cut out of cardboard.)*
Elena, I'm here, in the bar, across the street from your house.
(*The shadow moves slowly, a hand pulls aside the curtain. It is a moment of heart-rending emotion . . . She appears. And they see each other from a distance, after thirty years, each of them with a phone receiver to their ear. But she is somewhat in the dark, against the light, it's impossible to make out her features. Her voice gives a sudden start, instantly controlled.)*

VOICE ON TELEPHONE: Certainly, I remember . . .

(SALVATORE's *eyes glisten, try to pierce the distance and the darkness to get a better look, but in vain.)*

SALVATORE: Elena. I'd like to see you . . . Let's meet.

(ELENA *lets the curtain drop and goes back to being a shadow. She whispers the words.)*

VOICE ON TELEPHONE: It's been so long. Why should we meet? What good would it do?

SALVATORE: Please, don't say no . . .

(*But her voice is firm, unshakeable, even if quivering with emotion.)*

VOICE ON TELEPHONE: I'm old, Salvatore. And you too. It's best not to meet. Goodbye.

(*The shadow hangs up, disappars. The light goes off.)*

112: DIFFERENT SETTINGS. INT/EXT. EVENING
The wind is stronger now, the streets and the square are empty.
SALVATORE *is at the wheel of the car, driving aimlessly around the*
town. He has rediscovered the woman who conditioned his whole life
and they hadn't had the courage to meet. An obsessive musical beat,
fraught with rage, pours out of the car radio.

113: SALVATORE'S MOTHER'S HOUSE. INT. EVENING
A phone ringing drowns out the sound of the television and the wind
whistling outside. In the half-darkened room, MARIA *picks up the*
receiver . . .
MARIA: Hello?
> (*No one answers, but she can sense the presence of someone who*
> *now hangs up.* MARIA *is alarmed. Who could it be at this hour?*
> *And where is Totò?*)

114: SEAFRONT AND PIER. EXT/INT. CAR. EVENING
SALVATORE *stands motionless on the pier, facing the storm-tossed sea.*
He feels relieved by the roar of the waves that dispels his bitter
thoughts, blurs them, but does not wipe out the look of suffering in his
eyes. A flashing light seems to approach behind his back. SALVATORE
turns and is blinded by the headlights of a car parked at the beginning
of the pier. The splattering waves lend the scene a hazy cast and
diffuse the glare of the flashing headlights. Now the lights move
towards him. And SALVATORE *also takes a few timid steps forward.*
They are close. The car has almost stopped. But it is impossible to
make out the person at the wheel who now reaches over to open the
other door. A voice can be barely heard over the raging sea. It is
ELENA'*s voice.*
ELENA: Salvatore!
> (SALVATORE *approaches, accepting the invitation, enters the car*
> *and shuts the door. The headlights go off and the car remains*
> *there suspended between the open sea and the harbour with its*
> *rocking boats.*
> *Inside the car, not a word. Two dark figures gaze at each other,*
> *unintelligible, as if the night were trying to further delay that*
> *meeting. The glowing reflection of a wave higher than the others*
> *now lights up their faces.* ELENA *was right: they are no longer the*
> *faces of teenagers, but of people on in years who study each other,*

84

*searching for a truth. The howling of the wind and the crashing
of the waves are louder, but* ELENA *and* SALVATORE *hear
nothing, sit glued to their seats, fixed in the endless gaze that
envelops them. He is the first to break the silence in a faint
voice.*)

SALVATORE: How'd you know I'd be here?

ELENA: I don't know how many years have gone by, but some
things about you I *do* remember. There weren't many
places you could have gone. I looked around . . .

(SALVATORE *turns on the light of the rear-view mirror. Finally
they can see better. They look at each other a little ill at ease,
making the inevitable comparisons with the memory of their
young faces.* SALVATORE *carefully observes her greying hair,
her blue eyes lined with wrinkles, the somewhat faded beauty
mark on her lip.*)

SALVATORE: You're still beautiful . . .

ELENA: Don't be silly . . . I'm old.

(*She looks down, troubled by the way he has of gazing into her
eyes, speaks almost mumbling her words.*)

Don't look at me like that, please.

(*And she switches off the light. But this time it is less dark,
things can be seen.*)

Why'd you come back?

SALVATORE: Alfredo died. Do you remember him?

ELENA: Of course I remember him. I'm sorry. You were terribly
fond of him.

(*A moment of silence. It's hard to find something to say.*)

SALVATORE: I saw your daughter. She's beautiful! Who knows
how many Salvatores must be running after her . . .

ELENA: (*Smiling*) One or two. But there're not all that many
Salvatores.

(SALVATORE *also smiles, but a puzzled smile as if what she has
said had thrown him off-guard.*)

I've got a son, too . . . he's older. And you, do you have
children?

SALVATORE: No. And I'm not married.

(ELENA *sits there in silence. A veil of sadness clouds her eyes.*
SALVATORE's *too . . .*)

Are you happy?

ELENA: All things considered, yes. Even if it wasn't what I dreamt of then . . .

(*Again* SALVATORE *is thrown off-guard, as if the round key of his enquiry had met with only square locks. She continues.*)

ELENA: My husband . . . you know him.

SALVATORE: Sure, sure! Boccia . . . (*With a bitter smile*) What's he do?

ELENA: Politics. He's the district representative. We met at the University in Pisa.

(*Then instinctively, in a shy voice,* SALVATORE *asks the question that he probably wouldn't have asked a moment later.*)

SALVATORE: And . . . how come you never married that guy from Tuscany?

(*The white foam of the waves splashes up over the wall of the pier, dashing against the car windows. The shadow of the trickling water is superimposed on the agony of their faces.*
ELENA *hides her embarrassment beneath a faint but haughty smile.*)

ELENA: I didn't want to . . . I had to fight tooth and nail. But in the end I won . . .

(SALVATORE *is unable to smile. It's as if the void were growing and swelling within. Thunder and lightning shatter the roaring of the wind and sea, but it does not rain. Now her smile fades away.*)

At that time . . . I was waiting for you . . .

(*There is no resentment in her words. She has said them fondly. With the serenity of someone who has suffered greatly and then found a strong convincing way of suffering no more. For* SALVATORE, *it's as if one of those thunderbolts had pierced his heart. He leans over, gazing into her shining eyes.*)

SALVATORE: But I've never forgotten you, Elena!

ELENA: (*Whispering*) Nor have I. Even though you disappeared . . .

(SALVATORE *is staggered, feels as if he were plunging into the void. What she has said strikes him as grotesque.* ELENA *strokes his hair, as if to restrain his sinking heart, gives a sweet smile.*) But what's the point of talking about it? We risk being pathetic and ridiculous.

(*And she tries to change the subject.*)

You still live in Rome?

(*But* SALVATORE *ignores the question. He doesn't want to change the subject. He feels that everything is crumbling inside him, the alibis and excuses he had had to give himself in order to accept the end of their romance. And instead, now the tables seem to have completely turned. Without realizing, he shouts desperately, staring wildly at her and shaking her by the shoulders.*)

SALVATORE: What do you mean, you were waiting for me?! What are you saying?

(*He controls himself at once, continues, breathing heavily.*)

The last time we saw each other, we made a date to meet at the Cinema Paradiso. You remember? And you didn't come, you disappeared without leaving a trace, nothing! *I'll* tell you how many years have gone by: more than thirty!!!

(*Quiet tears stream down* ELENA's *face, glisten with the reflections of the lightning and the waves.*)

ELENA: I kept that date.

(SALVATORE *laughs at the absurdity of it. A nervous, heartbroken laugh, which slowly melts away as she goes on to say:*)

But I was late . . .

(*Tears continue to stream out of her blue eyes, but she tells her story in a calm voice.*)

I had a fight with my family. I tried to convince them again that they couldn't separate us. But it was futile. They had decided to leave Sicily once and for all. Which is what we did. I didn't know what to do any more, what to say. And I said yes, I'd do whatever they wanted. In return, my father promised to let me see you one last time, to say goodbye. But I hoped that by seeing each other we could take advantage of it and make a decision . . . I thought we would run away together.

(*She holds back her sobs. Dries her tears with the back of her hand, and continues:*)

My father drove me to the movie theatre. But you weren't in the projection booth. Only Alfredo . . .

(*Her voice continues over the scene of some thirty years before . . .*)

87

115: CINEMA PARADISO. PROJECTION BOOTH. INT.
AFTERNOON
Flashback.

ELENA'S VOICE: (*Off-screen*) And I didn't have time to wait for you
to come back . . .
(*From the bottom of the spiral staircase,* ELENA'S FATHER *is
waiting nervously, yells up at the projection booth:*)
ELENA'S FATHER: Elena! Hurry up!!
YOUNG ELENA: All right, Daddy! . . .
(*In the projection booth,* ALFREDO *is sitting on a stool, near the
projector. Seen from the rear, the* YOUNG ELENA *is leaning over
beside him, she is excited, her eyes are red and swollen with tears.*)
ELENA'S VOICE: (*Off-screen*) So I told Alfredo how things stood
and that I was leaving the same evening, and I asked him to tell
you everything. He was very kind, he listened carefully,
then . . .
(ALFREDO *answers* YOUNG ELENA, *stroking her hair.*)
ALFREDO: Easy, easy. (*Sighing*) Listen carefully to what I have to
say. If you want me to tell Totò what you've told me, I will.
But if you want my advice, forget it. It's better for both of you
if you don't see each other . . .
(YOUNG ELENA *gives a start of resentment, listens with surprise.*)
Dear girl, fire always turns into ashes! Even the deepest love
ends sooner or later. And after that other loves appear, lots of
them. Totò, he can't understand that now. If I tell him he
won't believe it, he'd be capable of killing me . . . But you can
understand, you've got to understand . . . Do it for him!

116: WATERFRONT. INT. CAR. EVENING
SALVATORE *sits there without moving, pale as a sheet, looks as if he had
grown even older. As if the whole world has fallen in on him. For*
ELENA, *it was a painful but liberating story. She dries her last tears.*
ELENA: It's the first time I've had to chance to tell the story. I never
mentioned it to anybody.
SALVATORE: (*In a daze*) Alfredo, damn him! He cast his spell on
you too!
ELENA: I told him I'd take his advice. But before I went away I left
you that note . . .
(SALVATORE *gives her a quick look, a questioning look. He listens.*)

88

I was on my way down the stairs . . .
(*Her voice continues, laid over the* . . .)

117: CINEMA PARADISO. PROJECTION BOOTH. INT.
AFTERNOON
Flashback.
ELENA *has already said goodbye to* ALFREDO, *is on her way down the stairs, but stops short.*
ELENA'S VOICE: (*Off-screen*) I thought Alfredo couldn't see me. So I snuck back up . . .
(*She tip-toes back without making any noise. Goes over to the film-winder. Takes out a pen, looks for a scrap of paper, but doesn't see any. Her eyes fall on the film receipts hanging on the nail. She tears off the top one, turns it over and scribbles a message on the back.*)
I wrote you where you could find me, and that I'd wait for you.
(*She hangs the scrap of paper back on the nail, well in sight. She creeps out, glancing at* ALFREDO, *who hasn't noticed a thing.*)

118: WATERFRONT. EXT/INT. CAR. EVENING
ELENA *finishes telling her story. She heaves a deep sigh.*
ELENA: But you disappeared all the same.
(*There is a haunted look in* SALVATORE's *eyes, he is searching his memory for something he can't find, then suddenly sees, as if in a dream* . . . *his hand thirty years before going through the routine gesture of hanging a receipt on the nail, over the others, mechanically, without even looking* . . . *and he shuts his eyes as if fearing the truth. Her last words have wounded him. He shakes his head, then in a faint voice:*)
SALVATORE: Oh, how I looked for you, Elena! You'll never know. I wrote, telephoned, nothing. Nobody ever answered. But I dreamt of you for years! That's why I went away . . . and never came back here.
(*And his anguish breaks free, dissolving into quiet, almost childish tears.* ELENA *is startled by his reaction. She caresses him, passionately. They embrace and remain like that, she with her face buried in his shoulder, he leaning on hers with his tear-filled eyes.*)

Even as the years passed, in all the women I met, I was only looking for you. I had success it's true, but there was always something missing . . .

(*She is deeply moved, goes on caressing him gently until he calms down. The car windows are steamed up. The sea, the harbour, the waves have disappeared. Nothing remains but the sound of the storm.* SALVATORE *takes her face between his hands. They gaze at each other, their faces practically touching. He murmurs:*)
I'd never have imagined that all this had to end because of the man who was like a father to me. A crazy lunatic!

(*She gives a faint smile.*)

ELENA: He wasn't crazy. In the beginning I was upset. I think I really hated him. But then, with time, I understood what he said . . . and your silence too.

(SALVATORE *whispers one last dreadful revelation. And it's as if he had got a terrible weight off his chest.*)

SALVATORE: But I never saw that note!

(*He squints, as if to stress the absurdity of the idea.*)
I must have covered it with my hand, without realizing it, that's the only explanation.

(*But strangely enough,* ELENA *is not surprised.*)

ELENA: What difference does it make to find an explanation? That's the way it went. But Alfredo didn't betray you, he was the only one who really understood you. Salvatore, if you had chosen to be with me, you'd have never made your films. And that would have been a pity! Because they're wonderful, I've seen them all.

(*Her eyes glitter with joy, then she smiles, almost ironically.*)
But you shouldn't have gone and changed your name. You should have kept your own.

(*Tears stream down* SALVATORE's *cheeks. He gives her a look of longing, of desire.* ELENA *embraces him. They kiss with heart-rending tenderness, with the same passion of their first kiss amidst the strips of film brushing their faces, so many years ago. And they make love, clasped in the cramped quarters of the car, like two teenagers. Passionate kisses, embraces, deep sighs. Their hair damp with sweat, their hands clasping, their fingers interweaving. Then the frenzy subsides into a deep, tumultuous pleasure, of immense loving and immense grief . . . As outside the*

*wind and the waves go on raging around that car which seems
suspended in empty space.*)

119: ALFREDO'S WIDOW'S HOUSE. INT. DAY
SIGNORA ANNA's *hands place an old wooden stool and a rusty round
metal can on the table.*
ANNA: These are the things he left to you . . .
>   (SALVATORE *is sitting by the table. He has finished the cup of
>   coffee* SIGNORA ANNA *has prepared for him. He picks up the
>   stool, recognizes it at once: it's the one* ALFREDO *had made for
>   him as a little boy so he could climb up and put the reels on the
>   projector.*)
ANNA: When they showed your films on television, he was happy.
He'd plop himself down there and all his ailments were
forgotten. He knew all the words by heart, every one, and I'd
describe what was going on. And when the papers talked
about you, I had to read them two or three times . . .
>   (SALVATORE *examines the can, wonders what it can be. He
>   opens it: inside is a reel of film, wrapped in a plastic bag, well
>   preserved. Those objects bring a pang to his heart, and the things
>   that* ANNA *said, but he feels disappointed, as if he expected to
>   find something else.*)
SALVATORE: Did he ever think of meeting me?
ANNA: No, never! One time your mother said that if he wanted,
you'd have surely come. He got furious and said: 'No, Totò
mustn't come back to Giancaldo, never!!' He didn't say it to
be mean. He was a decent man. Who knows what he could
have been thinking? Towards the end he'd say such strange
things. And a moment before he shut his eyes, he told your
mother not to let you know.

120: CINEMA PARADISO. PROJECTION BOOTH. INT. DAY
*A cloud of yellowed scraps of paper flutters into the air and as it falls
slowly to the ground another handful is flung up.* SALVATORE *is in the
projection booth, looking through the countless yellowed receipts,
stuffed away in boxes. He looks at them one by one, then throws them
into the air. A desperate search, almost a defiance of the passing of
time.*
He continues with greater determination, flings piles of receipts into the

air, glances at a few dates, a film title, tries to discover the oldest dates at the bottom. He moves swiftly, his hands plunge in, then fling up a nimbus of paper and dust. But to no avail . . . He stops, short of breath. His eyes go over to the nails in the wall, where other stacks of receipts are hanging. He gets up and goes to look at them, thumbs through them hastily, in anger.

He yanks off two or three packs, which come off, nail and all. Only then does he notice that at the bottom of those blocks of yellowed paper, there are some more sheets, much older, almost brown. His eyes concentrate on the mildewed scraps of paper. He leans over, picks them up and goes through them one by one, delicately, because they crumble in his fingers . . . And then all of a sudden, some film titles he recognizes from that time. He goes on thumbing through them, and all at once an astonished look appears on his face: in his hands is a receipt that has been turned over. It's the one! The message scribbled on it can still be seen. He reads it.

SALVATORE'S VOICE: (*Off-screen*) Salvatore, forgive me. I'll explain later what happened. Not finding you here was terrible. Unfortunately, this evening, my mother and I are leaving for Tuscany. We're moving there. But you're the only one I love, I'll never be with anybody else, I promise. Here's the address of a girlfriend of mine where you can write to me. Don't abandon me. Love and kisses, Elena. (*He clasps the scrap of paper, and his brimming eyes darken with regret.*)

121: CAFÉ IN SQUARE AND ELENA'S HOUSE. INT/EXT. DAY
ELENA *stands near the window overlooking the little square, listening on the phone to* SALVATORE'*s voice. She can see him through the transparent curtain speaking on the phone down below in the café.*
ELENA: When are you leaving?
(SALVATORE *opens his eyes, tosses away his cigarette.*)
SALVATORE: This afternoon. Elena, in the future maybe we could . . .
(ELENA *interrupts him, speaks softly, tenderly.*)
ELENA: No, Salvatore . . . there is no future. There's only the past. Even meeting last night was nothing but a dream, a beautiful dream. (*Smiling*) We never did it when we were kids, remember?

(*Down in the café,* SALVATORE *nods his head slowly,
desperately.*)
Now that it's happened, I don't think there could have been
a better ending.
(*It's farewell.* SALVATORE *glances one last time at that
window.*)
SALVATORE: I'll never agree with you. Never, Elena.

122: CINEMA PARADISO. EXT. DAY
*The square, unusually empty. There is no one, and no cars and
motorcycles are parked in the middle. The stores are shut. And there is
an unreal silence. The houses on the two streets on either side of the
theatre are covered by enormous pieces of grey canvas.
Only now does the camera discover in the distance, a crowd of curious
onlookers waiting in front of the movie house, kept at a safe distance
by firemen and policemen. Old* SPACCAFICO *is in the crowd.*
SALVATORE *is also there. He gazes at the front of the old movie
theatre* . . .

123: CINEMA PARADISO. INT. DAY
The inside of the theatre, completely empty . . . *All of a sudden, a
blinding flash and* . . .

124: SQUARE AND CINEMA PARADISO. EXT. DAY
. . . *a deafening roar rends the air, accompanied by a surge of
amazement in the crowd. And the Cinema Paradiso suddenly
collapses, folds inward and disappears for ever in a gigantic cloud of
white smoke that rises into the air, carried by the wind towards the
crowd* . . .

125: ELENA'S HOUSE. INT. DAY
The echo of the explosion is also heard in ELENA'*s house. She is alone.
And the bang distresses her, as if something had burst inside her.
From her face to* . . .

126: SQUARE AND CINEMA PARADISO. EXT. DAY
SALVATORE'*s face, stiff, unmoving, his eyes fixed on those falling
ruins, on that season of his life turning into smoke and dust.
Enveloped in the white cloud,* SPACCAFICO *stands crying in silence.*

93

Mice dart out of the ruins in terror, scamper nervously into the square.
A group of youngsters scream, amused and excited. Among them,
ELENA'S DAUGHTER, *smiling . . .*
SALVATORE *sees her joking with friends and pointing to some boys*
chasing the mice across the square, hooting and laughing. As a white-
haired OLD TRAMP, *filthy and covered in rags, makes his way*
through the crowd. There is an empty look in his eyes and he repeats
obsessively in a low voice:

VILLAGE IDIOT: The square's mine, the square's mine, the
　　square's mine . . .

　　(SALVATORE *recognizes him, it's the* VILLAGE IDIOT, *the one*
　　who used to close down the square at night. He watches him walk
　　off, raving, with nobody even noticing.
　　The crowd now moves over to the huge empty space where the
　　movie house once stood. The murmuring voices are drowned out
　　by the deafening roar of an airplane. From the ruins of the
　　Cinema Paradiso, fade to . . .)

127: ROME. STUDIO VIEWING-ROOM. INT. DAY
. . . SALVATORE's *hands giving a* STUDIO PROJECTIONIST *the rusty*
metal can left him by ALFREDO.

SALVATORE: Please check the splices. As soon as you're ready you
　　can start.
PROJECTIONIST: OK. Congratulations on your film. It's terrific.
SALVATORE: Thanks.
　　(*A* COLLEAGUE *of* SALVATORE *comes up behind him.*)
SALVATORE: Well?
COLLEAGUE: The distributor is opening up the film earlier. The
　　press conference is in the afternoon. The actors will also be
　　there, the producer, just about everyone.
　　(*An* ASSISTANT *comes up to them.*)
ASSISTANT: The official notification of the award just came out,
　　but we've already received a mountain of telegrams. Aren't
　　you happy?
SALVATORE: It's all right. We'll talk about it later.
　　(SALVATORE *walks off towards the viewing theatre.*)

SALVATORE *is by himself in the small viewing theatre. Now the lights*
go down. The beam of light shines out of the little square hole of the

projection booth and the screen lights up. A number trailer goes by and then SALVATORE *sees the first shots. A start of intense amazement and joy suddenly runs through him, astounds him, delights him. It's the best piece of film he has ever seen . . .*

It consists of all the kisses ALFREDO *cut out of the films and kept for him, when he was a little boy. They have been spliced together, one after the other, at random, some of them even upside down. And yet it looks like a first-rate editing job. In rapid sequence the passionate kisses between actors and actresses, names famous and names unknown in the history of movies. Greta Garbo, Gary Cooper, Alida Valli, Rudolph Valentino, Ingrid Bergman, Clark Gable, Anna Magnani, Humphrey Bogart, Marlene Dietrich, Amedeo Nazzari, Luisa Ferida, Vittorio De Sica, Rita Hayworth, Tyrone Power, Doris Durante, Massimo Girotti, Marta Abba, Fred Astaire and Ginger Rogers, Assia Noris . . .*

A whole movie season summed up in a few fragments, a few seconds. A bizarre, poignant, melancholy parade.

SALVATORE *is overwhelmed, moved to tears. It is the most profound act of love he has ever seen. He laughs as tears shine in his eyes. Up on the screen, another kiss, the last kiss marking the happy ending of a film. And the age-old words appear:* 'THE END'.